SLATE QUARRYING
IN WALES

Slate Quarrying
in Wales

by
Alun John Richards

Text © Alun John Richards, 1995

ISBN: 0-86381-319-4

Cover: Ffestiniog Railway at Tanygrisiau

First published in 1995 by Gwasg Carreg Gwalch,
Iard yr Orsaf, Llanrwst, Gwynedd, Wales.
☎ (01492) 642031

Printed and published in Wales.

Contents

Appendices

Acknowledgements

Grateful thanks for research assistance are due to —
Dr David Gwyn
Griff. R. Jones
Gwynfor Pierce Jones
William T. Jones
Dr Michael Lewis
Dr Lewis Lloyd
Steffan ab Owain
Dafydd W. Price
Jeremy Wilkinson
Merfyn Williams
Richard Williams
The staff of the National Library of Wales
The staff of the Gwynedd Archives Service, Caernarfon
and Dolgellau
The members of Fforwm Tan y Bwlch

For background material, my many friends involved or formerly
involved in the industry.

For general help, encouragement and the use of the Snowdonia
National Park Study Centre —
Peter Crew,
Twm Elias,
Robin Jones.

And for tireless practical archival and fieldwork input and for
proof reading, my wife Delphine.

Grid references of sites mentioned are in the Site List. (Appendix
1)

Should this encourage the visiting of such sites to see the relics of a once great industry, it must be remembered that all are on private land and permission of the owner must be obtained before doing so, also the consent of the occupier of any ground which has to be crossed to reach a site.

Abandoned slate quarries are dangerous. Rock is slippery, tips can move, falls can and do occur, portions of structures can collapse. There may be hidden and unguarded precipices and shafts. Underground workings should never be entered other than as a competently led and properly equipped party.

For a fuller list of locations see A Gazeteer of the Welsh Slate Industry by Alun John Richards (Gwasg Carreg Gwalch).
ISBN 0-86381-195-5.

1. In The Beginning
Up to the late 18thC.

In parts of Wales, particularly in the north west, great mounds of slate waste, the detritus of a once great industry, glower over the landscape, silently reproachful of that industry's decline. On the skylines the walls of ruined drumhouses stand like twinned cenotaphs commemorating its triumphs and tragedies. Slates cover the roof, and sometimes the sides as well, of every house. Slate blocks form almost every building and wall. Slate slab is underfoot as steps and pavings, 'planks' of slate make fences. Almost every man-made artifact seems to be of the one, universal material.

Although its origins are ancient and its saga continues, slate was very much a Victorian industry. Apart from its era almost exactly matching that monarch's reign, its bold, innovative development reflected the spirit of that age. It dominated the economy of the north-west of Wales, where, by the middle of the 19thC. it accounted for almost half the total revenues from trade, industry and the professions, and in Wales as a whole, its output value compared with that of coal.

Slate quarrying has been described as the 'Welshest' of industries, for unlike metal or coal mining, and iron or tinplate manufacture, its techniques were almost all locally devised. Dominating British, even world output, it was manned almost exclusively by native Welshmen who sprang from the same soil as the rock they worked and it is said, have a temperament uniquely suited to the working of this recalcitrant stone. Paradoxically although the language of the quarry, its tools and its methods was, and still is, exclusively Welsh, there is no Welsh word for slate. Llech or Llechfaen, can be applied to any flat stone. For instance the Welsh Bible refers to Moses being ordered to hew two 'lechau cerrig' (Exodus XXXIV, 1) this does not infer that slate outcropped on Mount Sinai, but is a literal translation of the Hebrew 'Flat Stone'. Also any flooring flag regardless of its geology may be called 'llech'. Thus it may be difficult to

8

distinguish between slate and other stone in historical records. The modern term 'slat' or 'slatten' is used, but correctly only for a writing slate. A tile in Welsh is 'Priddlech', literally an earthslate. The not uncommon place name Llechwedd, has no slate connotation, it merely denotes a flat hillside.

The industry brought prosperity to Bangor and Caernarfon, it created towns such as Bethesda, Blaenau Ffestiniog, Llanberis and Porthmadog, and biblically named hamlets such as Bethel, Carmel, Seion and Salem. It vitalised villages such as Corris, Dolwyddelan, Deiniolen, Penygroes and Talysarn. Above all, it created a whole new and proud way of life.

Welsh slate is a metamorphosed sedimentary rock, generally mudstone, which has been subjected, by volcanic action and earth movements, to great pressures and temperatures. This has caused the rock to become grain orientated along parallel planes, which are independent of and at an angle to the original bedding planes. This gives it a potential to be divided along these cleavage planes into impervious, durable laminae of relatively great strength, which made and still makes it a valuable and unique material. Probably unique too, is the fact that, unlike other minerals slate is extracted and manufactured into a totally finished domestic product, on the same site. The method of conversion has, mechanisation apart, remained substantially unchanged to the present time.

Its most commonly recognised use is as a roofing material, whose lightness and permanence, even today, no substitute material can surpass. However, almost half the tonnage during the 19thC. was in Slab, widely used for flooring, fireplaces, cills, lintels and quoins. Its imperviousness made it ideal for brewers and chemical vats. It was used for cisterns, originally carved from the solid, but later sold as sets of drilled and grooved pieces with appropriate rodding, like modern self-assembly furniture. It was also an ideal material for lining pigsties, cowsheds and so on, as well as those monuments to Victorian civilisation, the 'Gentlemens'. Its high specific heat, made slab useful in dairies and larders. Later its dielectric properties, would be exploited for switchboards. It is still used for billiard tables, although sadly, no longer sourced in Wales. Among slate's more bizarre uses was for the making of coffins.

Most famously, slab was used for that inviolable Welsh tradition, the slate gravestone. Carved and epitaphed headstones began to sprout in their serried ranks during the 18thC. But for long before that graves were marked by rough-hewn slabs, laid flat on the ground and normally bearing only initials and date of death.

Although the term 'Slate Grey' is in common use, slate colours, due to chemical inclusions, vary from grey through blue to green, purple and red, with some being almost black[1]. These colorations were capitalised on, not only for roofing but for the 'decorative' objects indispensable to the Victorian home. As if these colours were not enough, there grew up in the second half of the 19thC., a whole mini-industry devoted to applying an enamelled finish to slate products.

Welsh slate occurs in 3 geological series; Cambrian, Ordovician & Silurian, being respectively around 600, 500 & 400 million years old. Slate is found in veins which though extensive, can obviously only be worked where they are near the surface. The rock must exhibit clean, parallel cleavage, be free of jointing and other interruptions that would limit the size of block extracted, yet have enough jointing to facilitate extraction. There needs to be a minimum of inclusions marring the appearance, integrity and durability of the product, and it is desirable that the plane of cleavage should not be at too small an angle from the bedding plane.

Some of the most important veins where the earliest commercial extraction mainly took place, are those Cambrian series which run south-west in a swathe from Conwy towards Pwllheli, the most abundant good cleavable rock being in the immediate hinterland of Bangor and Caernarfon. These gave rise to the 'superquarries' of Penrhyn, at Bethesda, and Dinorwig on the northern shore of Llyn Padarn, as well as other smaller workings neighbouring them. These same veins attracted early quarrying on Mynydd y Cilgwyn to the east of Penygroes, which spread to eventually almost fill the

Nantlle valley. Outcrops also occurred on Cefn Du, south-west of Llyn Padarn and in the Gwyrfai valley south-east of Waunfawr. Somewhat less desirable rock has been worked in the lower Conwy valley, though much, particularly to the east of the river, is not true slate, being flaggy material which only divides along the bedding planes. There are also isolated workable occurrences on the coast near Harlech, and inland at Trawsfynydd. The two small quarries in Anglesey, Llaneilian & Llanfflewyn are also on Cambrian rock.

The other substantial slate Veins are the Ordovician, running south west from around Betws-y-coed to Porthmadog, being at their richest and best around Blaenau Ffestiniog, tapering off to less desirable, but still exploitable rock, on either side. Ordovician rock also occurs to a lesser extent in a broad, less continuous band, running parallel some miles further south, from Llangynog to Aberdyfi, with the best rock mainly around Corris. In fact these two occurrences, respectively north and south of the Harlech Dome, were once part of the same great anticline. The relatively small and scattered occurrences of slate rock of south-west Wales, are also Ordovician.

Silurain slate, is found to the north and south of the Dee valley, in the Llangollen — Corwen area, in Glynceiriog to the east of Chirk and triflingly, in the Dulas valley north of Machynlleth.

Generally, it is the Cambrian series which provides the hardest and most durable slate, and the Silurian the least so, with the Ordovician in between. But since geological action is not regular, this can only be the broadest of generalisations. The Ordovician of Blaenau Ffestiniog, particularly the Old Vein, makes excellent roofing material and some of the Corris Narrow Vein, exceptionally good slab. The Silurian from some of the Dinbych quarries yields good slab, particularly for indoor use.

It is not possible to clearly define the beginning of the Welsh Slate Industry. Some late Iron Age burial sites incorporated slate slabs, but since they were presumably used because they were handy flat stones and not because of intrinsic properties of the rock, this cannot be considered a true slate use. The Romans certainly recognised the properties of slate, as the surviving 3rdC.

flooring at Segontium (Caernarfon) testifies. This was of the Cambrian series and clearly from a local source. The origin of the somewhat earlier use at Caer Llugwy, near Capel Curig, of Silurian material is less obvious, suggesting that the nearer Cambrian deposits were then unknown. A slate tanning tank from Brithdir, near Dolgellau, of late Roman date, possibly suggests a source in the area, and if, as is widely believed, the slate slabs present in the Sarn Helen in the Migneint, are original surfacing, then Roman use of Ffestiniog slate is indicated.

In post Roman times, slate blocks were used for building and for household objects such as bakestones and scrapers, but there is scant evidence of slate roofing until the 12thC., and then only for the most prestigious buildings close to sources of supply. In the 13thC., it was rather more widely employed, most notably by Edward 1 for his castles, although, even at Caernarfon, built within sight of an abundant source of slate, timber and lead were the main roofing materials. When Edward 1 stayed at Nantlle, it is reported that he slept under a slate roof, suggesting that, (a), this was a sufficiently unusual happening to be worthy of record, and, (b), that slate quarrying was being carried out at nearby Cilgwyn.

In the 14th century repairs were made to Chester castle, reputedly with slate shipped coastwise from Aberogwen, near Bangor, presumably originating from Cae Hir, near what is now Bethesda. In 1399 a French poet, Creton, referred to the King (Richard II) arriving at Conwy 'where there is much slate'. This slate may have come from early diggings such as Llechlan or even have been brought down the river from the Machno or Lledr valleys, a trade which by that time was long established, both for local use and coastwise shipment. In the early 16th century repairs to Conwy castle were carried out with slate, but this probably came from Aberogwen, the likely source of slate for its original 1280s construction. Certainly during the 1500s permissions were granted for slates to be dug on the Penrhyn estate for shipment from Aberogwen and Abercegin to Chester, Ireland and elsewhere. In the late 16th century, Bishop Morgan (The translator of the bible into Welsh), specified this same material for the re-roofing of the cathedral at St. Asaph. (When work was done on the roof in 1932 these same slates were found to be sound and re-useable). Also in the 16th century there is a record of slates from Aberogwen being sought for shipment to Rhuddlan.

By the 15th century in Dyffryn Conwy, slate had become a commonplace roofing material for the more important houses, and in the 16th century with the building of a number of large houses in north Wales, slate roofs became more widespread as did small scale quarrying. By the mid 16th century there were shipments from Caernarfonshire to Ireland of perhaps 80 tons per year, which by the late 17th century had trebled, accompanied by a considerable growth in the home trade. Certainly by the 17th century men in many locations were describing themselves as Slaters, a term which implied extracting and making slates as well as laying them.

The winning of slate was not confined to the north-west. Quarrying at Bryneglwys, at least on a small scale, is believed to date from the 14th century. Certainly in the early 1500's Plas Aberllefenni, near Corris, was slate roofed, probably from Hen Gloddfa, later part of Aberllefenni quarry. A century later, John Leland remarked on the number of slate roofs to be found in Oswestry. These probably came either from Llangynog or from Glyn Ceiriog. Also at that time slate was being used in Wrexham, undoubtedly from quarries on Oernant, north of Llangollen, and from Llantisilio. A hundred years later this had become a regular trade.

In south Wales too, there was early use. It has been suggested that the Romans used Pembrokeshire material at Caerleon. Slate used to repair Carmarthen Castle in 1338, may well have come from the small quarries near the town. In the 16th century there were shipments through several south west Wales ports, such as Cardigan and Haverfordwest. By the end of the 17th century this had become a small, but established trade, with quarries such as Glogue being very much in business.

It must not be forgotten that well into the 18th century Wales, particularly north-west Wales was a remote region with poor communications. There was some trade with Ireland, but cattle droving apart, little with England. Wales was on the way to nowhere. The more mountainous areas were virtually devoid of roads, and even in the lower regions, such roads as there were, were of doubtful utility in Summer and almost impassable in Winter. Turnpike Trusts were established in Caernarfonshire in 1769, but even villages of some size had no road access until the early 19th century.

The maintenance of non-turnpike roads was a parish responsibility, inhabitants being theoretically obliged to participate in their maintenance. This obligation tended to be enforced only at the whim of the few big proprietors, who owned most of the land, and isolated from the seat of government, ran their fiefdoms with almost feudal authority. Moreover when a landlord called for road repairs it was more likely to be in the hope of exacting fines for non-compliance than any wish for improvement. It was not until 1827 that Parish Rates brought about 'professional' maintenance, but even then upkeep was minimal. The standard vehicle was the sledge, possibly horse, but more likely ox or even man pulled, wheelwrighting being a rare occupation. On the farms much 'cartage' was done with wheel-less barrows, like funeral biers. Thus no commodity, let alone one as heavy and breakable as slate, could be conveyed any great distance, save by water, the reaching of which called for the expensive use of pack-horses or mules, failing which, product had to be carried away on the backs of the men who won it.

Slate was, other than right alongside where it was dug, a material for the rich, and the rich were thin on the ground. Agriculture largely on unproductive, acidic hillsides, was at a subsistence level. Fishing served only very localised markets, woollen manufacture was carried out on home looms for pittances. In some districts metal mines provided ill-paid employment, but profits went to absentee landlords and distant proprietors. There was virtually no middle class. Few doctors could be afforded, few lawyers were needed, there was little coin to support shopkeepers and tiny tenant farms, produced no surplus wealth. Contemporary accounts euphemistically described the Welsh diet as, *'abstemious'* with *'animal food and ale not among their usual fare'*. One roomed hovels abounded, the better ones built of rough stones, some just 'mud and sod', the sparse accommodation frequently shared with a pig or a cow. Tenancies 'At Will' offered no incentive for occupiers to make improvments. Roofs were thatched with straw or fern or at best wooden shingles, with an aperture for the smoke of the peat fire. Some of the larger, owner-occupied farmhouses were slated, but there was little chance of the roofs of tenanted properties being slated, as customarily thatch maintenance was the occupier's responsibility whereas 'stone' roof repairs fell on the landlord.

Custom for slate being limited, and money for investment non-existent, Welsh slate for centuries remained a 'cottage' industry, little groups of men supplying the wants of the less indigent people of their immediate localities or the more affluent further afield. It was literally a cottage industry at Cwm y Glo[2] at the northern end of Llyn Padarn, blocks dug from where Glynrhonwy quarry would later be sited, were brought back by boat for reduction into roofing slates in the homes.

The rock was mostly extracted by crowbarring or driving iron wedges into cracks or natural joints. Assisted if necessary by wetting wooden wedges or quicklime. (In the sea-cliff quarries of south west Wales, the high tide could serve to soak wedges.) Fire-setting, ie heating rock then quenching to shatter it, may also have been used but tales of this being employed in the 20th century are probably apocryphal. After discarding unsuitable rock, hammers were used to reduce good blocks to manageable size for splitting. Methods were little changed from those in Pembrokeshire in the 16th century when they were described by Owen as *'The stone being digged in the quarry is cloven by iron bars to a thickness of a foot or half a foot and in length or breadth ii or iii foote and so carried for walling stones, or for tyle they cleave the same to what thines they thinke best, and so the self-same stone and quarry serveth to begin and end the house'*.

The smallness of scale is illustrated by the continued use of the old units of 'Cant bach' (Small hundred) of 32 and the 'Cant mawr' (Big hundred) of 128 based on half and twice a pannier load of 64, respectively. It was well into the 18th century before the nominal thousand or 'Mille' (1200 slates to user, 1260 to merchants), came into full use.

During the 18th century, things started to change, the Industrial Revolution was beginning, not that north west and mid Wales saw much of it. The iron and coal of the south and of Dinbych were remote, the textile and the various industries of midland and northern England even more so. But Britain like the rest of Europe was starting to move from agriculture to manufacture, trade was expanding, country dwellers were becoming townies, and a measure of prosperity loomed. In the remoter parts of Wales, apart from where metal extraction expanded, such as on Parys mountain, Anglesey, these events were bad news. Woollen production was moving into factories in border towns such as Newtown and Llanidloes, arable agriculture was marginalised by the agrarian developments of eastern and southern England. Rural Wales, particularly in the north west could well have slid into desperate want. Indeed in the 1730s there were disturbances in Bangor, protesting at the shortage and cost of basic necessities. Similar disturbances occurred at Pwllheli in 1751 and in 1766 mobs at Caernarfon tried to prevent a vessel being loaded with corn.

Paradoxically, this industrialisation, which could have been fatal to the frail, barter economy of north west Wales, was to provide its salvation. With the move from the country to the nascent industrial conurbations, houses were needed, and these houses needed roofs, lintels, fireplaces and the like. Thus, as the 18th century gathered pace, so did the demand for slate. It started to become something more than just a vernacular material for the poor or an exotic whim of the rich.

Activity increased particularly in north Caernarfonshire, where individuals holding Take Notes from the landowner, worked tiny diggings. These Take Notes were generally issued on an annual basis, almost always for a yearly rent of a few shillings plus a royalty either of an eighth or a tenth of the sale value, or a levy on tonnage or count. The terms usually specified that only one, or perhaps two men could work, additional helpers being often permitted at an extra annual charge.

Almost all Gwynedd slate went to market by sea, having been carried by whatever means possible, to the nearest tiny navigable creek. Much went to Ireland, the rest to English ports, a little found its way to such places as Dunkirk or Rotterdam. By 1730 shipments totalled about 2500 tons per annum. As trade developed, so did the size of ships, demanding the use of proper ports, benefiting such places as Caernarfon, from where, in 1730, 101 vessels sailed with an average of 16 tons of cargo. In 1792, 237 vessels left carrying an average of 35 tons.

When, due to transport constraints, loadings were still made at the tiny creeks, it became usual to trans-ship into sea-going vessels at an adjacent port. Such was the case for slate dug on Cilgwyn common, where by 1762, 8 of the diggings had developed into formal partnership quarries. Their product was carted to Foryd Bay, to be loaded into tiny boats for Caernarfon. The fact that a saving of only about 3 miles distance on comparatively good roads (and avoiding one or two tolls), justified this double handling illustrates the high cost of cartage. In the Conwy valley the loadings at Trefriw began to be increasingly trans-shipped at Conwy.

There was some trade inland. The industrialisation of the Wrexham area, provided a handy market for small diggings in north-east Wales, and some such as Craig yr Orin were regularly sending several hundred tons a year to the expanding English midlands, but the heavy costs of road cartage restricted this trade. Indeed Thomas Pennant referring to slate quarrying at Llangynog in 1778 said *'The want of water carriage is a great loss to the work.'*

Although slate digging was becoming more widespread, the great thrust was in the hinterland of Bangor and Caernarfon. As well as Cilgwyn, there was activity on the southern slopes of Mynydd Elidir, near the hamlet of Dinorwig, on the other side of Llyn Padarn on Cefn Du and, of course, at the head of the Ogwen valley on the Penrhyn estate.

On these barren tracts, landowners were obtaining small but useful revenues from slaters Take Notes. Not that such dues were always paid. The absence of a resident owner at Faenol meant that royalties at Dinorwig were not always collected, and where Crown land was involved, such as at Cilgwyn, the slaters were quick to take advantage of the Surveyor General's slackness in pursuing his tribute, giving those diggers a resented competitive edge. Not that they invariably prospered, for in 1752, 2 men were killed during a riot when needy Cilgwyn slaters raided a granary.

From at least the beginning of the 16th century, the Penrhyn estate (including lands to which it had doubtful title) had been a predominant source of slate. Rents, royalties and the profits from any sales undertaken on the slaters behalf was an important part of its income. But a decade or two into the century, Cilgwyn competition was causing takings to decline. The Cilgwyn slaters, apart from often paying little or no royalties or rents, had more easily worked rock, could make thinner and lighter, hence more cheaply transported slates. They marketed aggressively, developing a strong Irish as well as some Liverpool trade, where the reputation of their product was such that they could get a landed price of 14/- (70p) per Mille of 1200. Penrhyn product only fetched 13/- (65p) which represented a net figure to the diggers, after paying an onerous 2/8 (13.3p) royalty, of only around 5/ (25p). In 1738, Sir William Yonge and General Hugh Warburton, joint owners of the estate, alarmed at the fall in Penrhyn tonnage halved royalties to encourage trade. This move failed, by 1746 Penrhyn output had fallen to a mere 250 tons, a tenth of the Cilgwyn total. With quarrymen now netting as little as 3/6 (17.5p) per mille, (a fair week's output per man), royalties were again reduced to 10d (4.17p).

Though Penrhyn's sales efforts were at this time becoming increasingly ineffectual, it did make one decisive and far reaching contribution to the marketing of Welsh slate, the standardisation of sizes.

Traditionally sizing had been very haphazard, such terms as tefyll (slices), ysglodion (chips) and ysgyrion (splinters) were used, apparently without any defined dimensions. By the mid sixteenth century, some slates were being sold, sized as 'Singles' (usually

10″ x 5″) and later, 'Doubles' (usually 12″ x 6″), but consignments were frequently of random sizes. From a load, a roofer would first lay the largest, gradually going down to the smallest as he worked towards the ridge, giving rise to the graduation still to be seen on some old roofs. These early slates were fixed by a single oak peg and thus had a tapered top. They could be as much as ¾″ thick (up to six times the thickness of later slates). Since they were uneven and of trifling lap, moss packing was used to keep out rain. The term 'Moss Slates' persisted in use to describe very small slates long after this practice ceased.

With the need to establish standards for the increasing sizes of the rectangular 2 nail slates which the market was demanding, Warburton of Penrhyn, in 1738, devised the famous 'Female nobility' names. Already such was the influence of Penrhyn, that despite its then declining fortunes, this nomenclature soon became the Industry Standard, and with slight variations, remained so for almost two centuries. (Appendix 2).

Though there was some semblance of organisation emerging in Dyffryn Ogwen and Cilgwyn, most winning of slate remained a primitive operation of little gangs digging in holes wherever a promising outcrop presented itself, and making what use they could of such transport opportunities as there were. Typical of these fragmented workings was Bron y Foel, where product was carried in baskets to be put on board boats at Ynys Cyngar, just west of Borth y Gest, and at Portreuddyn, where it was carried a few yards to a beached boat, (before the Porthmadog Cob was built, it was almost on the shore).

Near Ffestiniog there were similar quarries such as Y Cefn and Cae'n y Coed, but further up the valley the outcrops in the tiny stream clefts were only worked when slate was needed for a roof or a gravestone. In about 1765 Methusalem Jones, an ex-Cilgwyn slate digger, whose spell as a publican, had no doubt brought him a modicum of prosperity, decided to return to quarrying. Guided, it is said by a dream, to this upper valley, he took a lease on part of the Wern estate at Diffwys, and started work. He brought other ex-Cilgwyn men into partnership, so forming one of the first ever quarrying 'firms' and founding what would become the great Blaenau Ffestiniog industry.

He faced a daunting task to get his product to market, it having to make a partly roadless journey down the mountain side to Maentwrog, where small boats could thread their way through the currents and sandbanks of the Dwyryd to seagoing vessels lying off Ynys Cyngar. A route probably pioneered some years earlier by Cae'n y Coed quarry, using the boats which brought supplies to Maentwrog.

Even when the slate was safely on board, the problems were not ended, as before the merchanting system was established, when cargoes were not bought outright by the ships' captains, a quarry owner had to see to the selling of the slate at its destination. Until bills of exchange became recognised in the late 18th century, he had to carry back the proceeds as well. One of the Diffwys partners, James Williams, is recorded as having walked to London in 1798, to arrange the sale of a cargo. Owing, presumably to war-time difficulties, he had to wait 3 months for the vessel to arrive, supporting himself by taking employment in a soap factory.

Thus in the late 18th century, the quarrying of slate was a burgeoning occupation, mainly centred in north Caernarfonshire, but it had not yet become an industry. That development, and the great improvements in transport, communications and commerce which it created, and the prosperity it brought, still lay in the future.

[1] — The blue colour is derived from protoxide of iron, the reddish and purple from iron peroxide. Black slate contains iron sulphide and carbonaceous matter, green slate has a low iron content, but is high in magnesia. The one totally undesirable inclusion, is iron oxide, which causes early failure, particularly in acidic industrial atmospheres. A combination of iron sulphide and calcium carbonates, can cause self-destruction even in benign environments.

[2] — Cwm y Glo translates literally as 'Coal valley', but probably derives from charcoal burning.

2. The Giants Stir
Late 18th Century — Early 19th Century

There is some doubt as to whether it was precisely 1765, when Methusalem Jones arrived at Blaenau, but it was certainly in that year when an event that was to have even greater significance to the industry took place. Susanna, only child of General Warburton, co-owner of the Penrhyn estate, married her kinsman, Richard Pennant M.P., son of John Pennant, a wealthy merchant. This wealth derived in part from fashionable estates in Cheshire and elsewhere and from less fashionable but vastly more profitable estates in Jamaica. At the same time Pennant senior was in the process of buying out Sir William Yonge's heir, Sir George Yonge, now the other co-owner of the estate.

In contrast to other landlords who, according to contemporary accounts, devoted their energies to *'Drinking, Betting and Whoring'*. John Pennant and Warburton took a close interest in affairs at Penrhyn. In particular their slate revenues which were being further eroded by the efforts of the Cilgwyn men.

In 1768, they tackled the problem by cancelling all Take Notes and substituting 21 year dead-rent leases, with strict conditions under which slate was to be raised. A Reeve was appointed to take charge of affairs at Abercegin and pay the slaters for whatever they raised. This seemingly shrewd move, obviated the continual collection of royalties and secured for them on the 54 leases an assured annual income of £80.

When John Pennant died in 1781, Richard sought ways of augmenting his substantial inheritance, perhaps anticipating his ennoblement as Lord Penrhyn in 1783. Leasing might have seemed a good idea in 1768, but in the intervening years many of the tenants, freed of the burden of royalties, had upped their tonnages, and on a firm market were in many cases making serious money. To Richard Pennant, this sort of thing would not do, and in 1782 he bought out the leases for a total of £160, and set about running things himself, offering employment to the dispossessed slaters.

It is impossible to exaggerate the importance of this event, for whatever view one may take of the subsequent history of the Penrhyn dynasty as owners and employers, from henceforward the working of slate in Wales could legitimately be called an industry. For the first time, slate was to be worked on a big scale, with adequate capital and with permanency of land tenure. The manager or agent was the able James Greenfield, who almost within a decade, had 500 men at work raising 15,000 tons per year, a good 50% more than the Cilgwyn/Nantlle men were putting out[1].

There was little difficulty in finding men. Farm workers on £5 per year (plus keep), found quarry wages of 10d (4.2p) per day attractive, particularly with the possibility of promotion to 'overlooker' on 1/ (5p), or even Bargain Setter at 1/4 (6.7p). Certainly by the early '90s when few men were making less than 1/, there was, in spite of the arduousness of quarry work, no incentive to return to the land, (although some men, having learnt how slate was won, took to the hills to start digging on their own account!)

Then in 1793, came the Napoleonic wars which though mightily beneficial to industries such as ironworks, was a body blow to slate quarrying. Building all but ceased, freight rates trebled, ships were captured by the French or their crews press-ganged and a heavy tax was imposed on coastwise shipments. On top of this there were seven consecutive years of bad harvests (1795-1801), which together with the sharp rise in living costs, brought much distress among quarrymen, leading to food riots in Caernarfon.

By the end of the century Penrhyn's output and manning was down by 75%. Pennant minimised his layoffs by deploying as many men as possible on improvements to the layout of the quarry and its transport arrangements. This foresighted benevolence enabled him to take full and prompt advantage of the recovery of trade which the new century brought. It is also to his credit that in 1798, aware of the hardships of his men, he provided a 100 acre site for them to plant potatoes.

At Dinorwig, on the other side of Mynydd Elidir, not dissimilar events to those at Penrhyn had taken place. Thomas Assheton on inheriting the Faenol estate in 1764, had tacked hyphen Smith onto his name and had taken up residence. In 1787, daunted by the task of organising his dozen or so Take Note diggers, he followed the Penrhyn example and put a stop to their individual workings. Unlike Pennant, Assheton-Smith did not take over himself, but granted a 21 year lease to the Dinorwig Slate Company, which was a partnership of 2 solicitors, Ellis and Wright and a Mr Bridges, described as a merchant (undoubtedly a slate merchant). They had problems as some of the doughty diggers, even in the face of force, continued to work on Dinorwig property. As late as 1809 'vagabonds' were still being reported, some allegedly tipping their waste in the company's workings. Expansion was less spectacular than Penrhyn, 1793 tonnage being less than 3000, but they seem to have been better able to maintain their output during the economic storms of the mid to late '90s.

In the Cilgwyn/Nantlle area and on Cefn Du, things were taking a different course. Most of the shipments from the numerous small quarries were going to Ireland, unaffected by the tax and less subject to war risks. But with no dominant private landlord and much of the ground being Crown land, the Penrhyn/Dinorwig pattern could not be followed. The first real organisation came in 1802 when John Evans, a prominent solicitor, John Price and Thomas Jones described as 'gentlemen', and Richard Roberts a slate merchant, leased Crown land and formed the Cilgwyn & Cefn Du Slate Company. They stopped unauthorised digging on their ground, (it had been reported in 1800 that there were over 120 'Trespassers' on Crown lands), and took the ejected men into employment. Cefn Du was some miles from Cilgwyn, but their commonality lay in that both areas would have carted to Caernarfon, where Roberts was selling and shipping slates. Later they took a number of other leases such as Gallt y Llyn and also took interests in Tal y Sarn, and Moel Tryfan. Similarly, in 1812, a syndicate of 2 slate merchants, a quarryman, and, oddly, a Stationer from Chester took over Cook quarry near Cefn Du, and were soon raising 500 tons per year. These firms were among the first of many which would reflect the interest both of local professional men and of slate traders in seeking profit from quarrying.

These slate merchants who were now becoming interested in quarry owning, were the successors to the north Caernarfonshire Reeves who saw to shipment and the finding of markets. Merchants became a formidable part of the slate trade, holding stocks for, and often advancing temporary finance to quarry operators. Also they were able to take into stock sizes or varieties that were in poor demand, very valuable in an industry where the type of product had to be determined by the out-turn of the rock rather than by market demand. Ultimately, virtually all business was done through them. Penrhyn's success was to a great extent due to their pioneering the appointment of merchants, and their selection of able and active ones such as Worthington of Liverpool.

The Reeves usual 18th century practice was to make a contract with an individual or partnership to take slate at a certain price, under certain conditions, for say, a 3 month period. This became the basis of the 'Bargain' system under which quarrymen worked for a proprietor. The Bargain system had roots in the Copper and Lead mining industries, and was to remain the basis of working right up to the mid 20th century. It entailed a gang making an agreement with the owner, or his Letting Steward, to work a particular stretch of rock. A rate would be negotiated of so much per mille of each size of roofing slate or so much per ton of slab, with additional payments for opening and the working of dead rock. Later there would be a permanent price list throughout a quarry, the men being paid on this plus a payment or 'poundage' intended to reflect the difficulty or otherwise of working and clearing a particular stretch of rock. Obviously the men would seek the highest rate of poundage whilst management would stand out for the lowest.

With goodwill and understanding the system could work well, but often these two virtues were not present when Bargains were being set. Also there was scope for unfair practices. A measure of nepotic or chapel based favouritism was one thing, but the out and out corruption, which became rife in some of the larger quarries, was quite another. This and ill-framed lists, could leave the Bargainers payless or even in debt to the employer (for powder, fuse, blacksmith work etc.) at the end of the letting period. The Bargain system was a cause of dispute in all but the smallest family-run quarries, well into the 20th century, yet it was stoutly defended by the Rockmen. This was partly because it gave an illusory feeling of independence, and partly because it distinguished the skilled men who won and reduced the rock, from the less skilled men such as the Rubblers who cleared away unusable material, and were paid on a daily or tonnage basis. When in 1823, Wyatt, the Penrhyn agent, concerned that some bargains were earning their teams £5 or £6 per 4 weeks others were, after deductions, sharing less than £1, offered to substitute a wage structure for the Bargain system, he got a dusty answer. Even as late as 1876, at Hafod y Wern, moves to phase out the bargain system caused a riot, and an attempt at Foelgron to devise a fairer system met with failure.

Initially at Penrhyn, gangs of anything from 2 to 12 men were tried, but by the late 1780s, 4-6 was the norm. Interim payments were made every 4 weeks with a full settlement (Tâl mawr) at the end of the 12 week Bargain period. (Later on Bargains were invariably of 4 weeks, with weekly intermediate 'subs'). A typical rate for Countesses, was 16/- (80p) per mille, Ladies half that and Doubles half that again. 'Ton' slates were rated at 8/- (40p) per ton. The quarry sold them at wharf for about twice those figures, but had to meet overheads such as the cost of breaking ground, clearing dead rock and cartage. But this still left a considerable profit.

Serious quarrying activity was also starting to spread. The Cilgwyn company took on Hafod y Wern and Garreg Fawr in Cwm Gwyrfai, midway between Cefn Du and Cilgwyn. Later they leased the little Ty'n y Ffridd quarry at Bethesda and Manod and Moelwyn at Blaenau Ffestiniog.

Times were changing too in other areas. The small tonnages loaded at Aberdyfi and Derwenlas, (the port for Machynlleth), were increasing. By 1797 Barmouth harbour was including slate in its list of tariffs, and cartage from Llangynog reached 2000 tons per year, and a little later slate was regularly coming from the Bala & Corwen areas.

At Blaenau, Methusalem Jones' partnership having struck the rich 'old Vein', had expanded, employing about 20 men, but in 1799 their landlord sold the lease to a syndicate of Lakeland men, William Turner and brothers David & William Casson. Turner had quarried in Ireland, then briefly held Clogwyn y Fuwch quarry, where he had overcome the problems of the vein underlying a great amount of overburden, by the Lake District method of quarrying underground. Evidence of Lakeland practice can still be seen at Clogwyn y Fuwch, with waste piled immediately outside adits, access being by corbelled tunnels, presumably to give protection from rock falling from the face above the adit. Working was by developing large 'caverns', a method Turner had used at Valentia in Ireland.

Under Turner's leadership Diffwys had a great decade of development, starting with the building of a road from the quarry to Cong-y-Wal, obviating the use of pack horses. They were amongst the first users of iron rails as opposed to wooden rails sheathed in iron (strapways). Almost uniquely they also used L section tramplates probably to 3'6" gauge. Later conversion to edge-rail on the same sleepers left them with track of 3'3¼" gauge. This together with the 2'2" gauge of the original edge-rail presented them with problems when 1'11½"/2' became the industry standard. (Except for the 2'3" of south Meirionnydd and the 2'4¼" of Glyn Ceiriog and Dinas Mawddwy).

Admittedly after Turner's time, but undoubtedly due to his influence, Diffwys pioneered extraction from the steeply dipping veins by working underground, a practice which was to become the mainstay of all Blaenau operations. The Cassons also built further roads and would make a wider impact when they established Casson's Bank, which by the 1840s had branches in Porthmadog, Blaenau Ffestiniog and Pwllheli. (It afterwards became part of the North and South Wales Bank, later absorbed by the Midland).

Alongside Diffwys, at Bowydd, some Take Note digging had commenced around 1780. In 1801, the landlord, Lord

Newborough, emulating Lord Penrhyn, took over the management. In spite of some road building, poor transport contributed to his lack of success. For the same reason, other openings to the immediate east, such as Bwlch y Slaters, Manod and Rhiwbach could not hope to greatly prosper.

At Dinorwig in 1809, following Ellis's death, Bridges dropped out and Wright was joined by Hugh Jones a Dolgellau banker and Assheton-Smith himself. Wisely, they lured William Turner from Diffwys with the offer of a partnership[2], and under his energetic management, set out to match the progress that had been made at Penrhyn quarry, beginning a rivalry that was to last a century and a half.

Both quarries had already improved their cartage, Dinorwig in fact leading the way when in 1788 they made road improvements, which eliminated pack-horses and cut their quarry to coast cartage costs from 10/- (50p) per ton, (more than the cost of production of the cheaper slates), to 6/6 (33p). Within two years Penrhyn had also completed roads, on which fleets of broad-wheeled wagons, each carrying up to 2½ tons, reduced cartage costs from 5/3 (27p) per ton to 4/- (20p). Pennant also made a road to Capel Curig in 1800, where he built the Eagles Hotel (now Plas y Brenin), perhaps to provide lodgings for acquaintances insufficiently eminent to be entertained personally.

Additionally, Pennant in 1790, overcame the 60 ton limitation on vessels using Aberogwen by establishing his own grandly named Port Penrhyn at Abercegin. Within three years Assheton-Smith had emulated him by making his own Port Dinorwig quay at y Felinheli, abandoning the use of Caernarfon. In time these ports became industrial units in their own right. At Port Dinorwig, after Rhys Jones moved his shipbuilding business from Barmouth in 1849, many substantial vessels were built. The refurbishment of ships, including prestigious steam yachts, continued into the 1960s.

However by the time the new partnership took over Dinorwig, all Penrhyn's road improvements were history, for in 1801 the Penrhyn tramway had been completed. This tramway was a pioneer, since at that time it was considered that only a canal could economically handle the sort of tonnages that Penrhyn was planning. In fact, a canal route had been surveyed by Thomas Dadford, the prominent canal engineer, but this was abandoned in view of the 550' fall in only 6 miles. The tramway's initial oval rail with concave waggon wheels was a mistake, (the track had to be relaid in edge-rail in the 1820s), as probably were the vertical drums used at the head of the 3 self-acting inclines, but it was in all other respects a model of its kind. Its lower end partly made use of the formation of an early line unconnected with the slate industry, which joined Abercegin with Aberogwen. The spacing of the inclines, Cilgeraint near the quarry, Dinas, part way along, and Marchogion, just short of the port, with constant and easy gradients between them whereby the horses could control the downgoing loads and readily haul back the empty wagons, made for efficient working. Its trackbed was well founded and the river Cegin was crossed and re-crossed by two fine stone bridges, one single, one triple arch, (which are still extant at SH593725 & SH722595). With trains of up to 24 waggons, pulled by 2 or 3 horses, each wagon carrying up to a ton (waggons were crewled down the inclines 3 at a time), it had a potential capacity well in excess of any then foreseeable tonnages. From the outset 16 horses and a dozen men did the work previously requiring up to 400 with some 140 drivers. Not only did the tramway reduce the cost of transport to the coast to around 1/- (5p) per ton, but it also freed the quarry from dependence on the whims of highly independently-minded farmers from whom most of the horses and carts were hired. Also horses were getting scarce and expensive, as apart from the war-time increase in feedstuff costs, in 1797 a tax on them was imposed to encourage their sale to the army.

Penrhyn's developments during the slack times of the 1790s, had included the gallery system of terraces at 65' — 70' vertical intervals. This enabled a large number of men to work simultaneously and reduced breakages by restricting the distance rock fell. Rail lines carried product in one direction to be lowered by balanced, self-acting inclines[3], and rubble the opposite way for dumping, the galleries being slightly graded to assist movement. This layout, subsequently widely copied, was to remain in use, virtually unchanged from Greenfield's original concept until the 1960s.

By the time of his death in 1808 Richard Pennant had not only more than recovered the lost business of the 90s, but had increased annual tonnage to 20,000, manning to over 600 and profits to a reputed £7000 per year. Moreover, he had consolidated his quarry as the dominant force in Welsh slate, and placed it in the forefront of innovation, his sandsaw mill being the first example of mechanisation on a serious scale. He introduced 'downstream' enterprises such as the writing slate, chimney-piece and tombstone factories at Port Penrhyn, which enhanced profits by adding value to the product. He considerably expanded his land holding, although in some cases under circumstances of doubtful legality. This gave rise to the saying — '*Steal a sheep, they hang you, steal a mountain, they make you a lord*'. He also laid down the 'model village' of Llandegai, anticipating the likes of Port Sunlight by almost a century. (This village of originally 40 cottages, had a church, but no tavern, and very definitely no chapel!)

The Dinorwig company, at first largely ignored the shortcomings of their roads, concentrating on technical improvements within the quarry. They put in galleries, of the Penrhyn pattern (but at slightly greater vertical intervals) and self-acting inclines which obviated the hazards described there by the Rev. W. Bingley in 1798.

'*The quarries are generally high up amongst the rocks, and the workmen, in conveying them down from thence, are obliged, as well as one horse before, to have another behind the carts, to prevent the whole, in some of the dangerous steeps in which these mountains abound, from being dashed headlong to the bottom, which must sometimes inevitably be the case without this contrivance. This seems a most inconvenient mode of conveyance: it appears that sledges, similar to those used in many parts of Westmoreland and Cumberland for conveying slates down the mountains, would not only be less expensive, but more safe and commodious'*. (Actually some inclines were probably already in use at Dinorwig by this time).

The same year Bingley also graphically described similar problems at Craig Rhiwarth, near what he sourly called '*The small and dirty village of Llangynog*'.

'*The quarries are high in the mountain; and I observed that the mode here of conveying them down was different from, and apparently much more dangerous than, that practised in the slate works about, near Llanberis near Caernarvon. Here they are placed on a small sledge, which by a rope, is fastened to the shoulders of the man who has the care of conveying it down, which is done along paths made for the purpose, which wind along the side of the mountain. He then begins to descend his face towards it; and, having firm hold with his hands, the velocity which the sledge acquires in its descent is counteracted by the man's striking against the prominences with his feet, which since he goes backwards, and has at the same time to keep the sledge on its track, must be a very difficult task, and can only be acquired by practice. The danger attending this mode of conveyance I should think must be very great; but upon enquiry at the village, I was informed that serious accidents have been very seldom known to occur*'. (This 600' descent was obviated in 1810 by the construction of an incline.)

Dinorwig further improved their cartage in 1812 by building a new road through Deiniolen. This obviated the loading of boats on Llyn Peris, taking them through a narrow cut to Llyn Padarn and rowing to Cwm y Glo for reloading onto carts for Caernarfon. Although by 1821 they had scrapped all barrows and carts within the quarry, there seems to have been no thought of an external rail link. It may have been Hugh Jones' caution as a banker, that held them back as directly the partnership was dissolved in 1820, and Assheton-Smith, took sole ownership, (retaining Turner as an employee on an eighth share of the profits), the problem of getting their product to the coast was addressed.

In 1824, the Dinorwig tramway was opened. It was inferior in many ways to the Penrhyn line. Its 3 inclines were ill-spaced. Not far from the quarry the Upper Cwm and the Lower Cwm inclines were only separated by an awkward loop and the long haul to the Garth incline, near the port, was unevenly graded. Its trackbed was not well built and its slate sleepers broke. Poor though it was, it reduced carriage costs to something near the Penrhyn figure, and gave Dinorwig a decisive competitive advantage over most of its competitors. By 1826 Dinorwig was employing 800, a fourfold increase in only six years, and were sending 20,000 tons of product a year down their new tramway.

In the Nantlle area, companies were being formed and quarries such as Penybryn, Gallt y Fedw, Tal y Sarn & Hafod Las, which had opened at the turn of the century were now all sending four figure tonnages to the Caernarvon quays. Fresh openings there continued, including in 1816 Pen yr Orsedd, one of several quarries in which the ubiquitous Turner was involved, and which would soon have a hundred plus payroll.

In the meantime, at Penrhyn, George Hay Dawkins, who had in 1816 inherited the property (but not the title) from the widow of his cousin Richard Pennant, added Pennant to his name and set about managing affairs. He is perhaps best known for his want of taste in building Penrhyn Castle, and for causing the first ever strike in the industry when in 1825 Greenfield having tragically died, he put the unpopular W. Williams in charge. However he did initiate direct shipments to America and made notable developments in the quarry such as the huge 16 sandsaw mill of 1816. By 1819 his payroll had risen from the 600 when he took over, to 800, producing annually over 24,000 tons, and before the 1820s were out, this was up to 40,000. Productivity had fallen from the excellent 33 tons per man year of 1808, to 30 t/p/m/y, mainly due to more men being employed in 'downstream' work, but it was still some 25% better than Dinorwig was able to achieve. With an average sale value in excess of £2 per ton, over twice the cost of production, net profits were running somewhat above the £80 p.a. his predecessors had been getting less than 40 years before.

Dawkins-Pennant followed his predecessor's example of extending his land holdings, not always successfully, for instance he started work at Tan y Bwlch and Bryn Hafod y Wern, but was

31

evicted. As late as 1849 (10th August) a Times leader referring to the practice of landowners improperly seeking to enlarge their holdings, instanced '*One common has been taken in without any shadow of right, which contains and is traversed by, the most gigantic and valuable vein of slates that has ever been worked or discovered in any part of the world*'. He continued his predecessor's practice of letting out leases for cottage building and making available materials, to 'good' workers. Usually the plot was big enough to allow wages to be supplemented by the growing of vegetables, the keeping of poultry, pigs or even a cow or two. Although the ground rents were modest, varying between 4/- (20p) and 10/- (50p) a year, the leases were short, so that after 30 years or so occupiers would see their property revert to the landlord and have to pay anything up to £4 p.a. to remain as tenants. Since this would cover rates and repairs, the terms were not onerous, but such tenants could and would be evicted if they ceased to be employed at the quarry, or if they pursued 'radical causes'.

Apart from the obvious problems of living in a home controlled by an employer, religion created difficulties. The majority of workers, were 'chapel', that is, they belonged to non-conformist sects such as Presbyterian, Methodist, Baptist and Congregationalist, all equally anathematic to Anglican owners. Thus they needed to live on non-quarry owned land, where they could build their biblically named places of worship, and establish schools under the 'British' and 'National' schools movements rather than the Anglican church schools dictated by the likes of the Pennants. The pre-eminence of the chapels being shown by the eponymous naming of the villages which grew up around them. S.G. Pattison, writing in 1869, clearly did not understand the fierce Non-Conformist Christianity of the Welsh slatemen when he questioned '*Why should this village on the river Ogwen where every sign and advertisement is in the Welsh language, derive its name from the pool by the Sheepgate of Jerusalem?*' He was of course referring to Bethesda where in 1820 a Congregational chapel was built on the Cenfaes estate, which, by 1871 would have a settlement whose population of 6297 would almost equal that of Bangor, Conwy &

Llandudno combined, with a total of 22 chapels. (This chapel building fervour was not confined to quarrymen, in Wales from 1800-1850, a new chapel opened every 8 days). This polarisation between Anglican, Tory management and Non-conformist, Liberal workers, would in future years exacerbate industrial relations particularly at Penrhyn and Dinorwig. Although it must be said that Assheton-Smith was less rigid in his Anglican stance than the Pennants, even on occasion, giving land for the building of chapels.

Also on land adjacent to, but outside the Penrhyn holding, some small-scale quarrying was going on, notably at Pant Dreiniog, Moel Faban, Tan y Bwlch and Bryn Hafod y Wern. They had a struggle to get their product to the coast, either to Aberogwen (where Pennant would not allow them to stack at the waterside) or to the less suitable Hirael jetty at Bangor.

Besides transport problems, marginal diggings, on poorer rock, were at a further disadvantage. The war having increased the price of timber, there was a call for bigger sizes of slates which required fewer roof battens. Thus the steep price increases of the early 1800s were largely confined to the bigger sizes. Quarries such as Penrhyn could readily produce these and Dawkins-Pennant, undoubtedly pushed the rates for them to the maximum that the market would stand. With his profit secured on the premium products, he could afford to clear the smaller and poorer varieties at prices little above 18th century levels. Since it was the Penrhyn list which ruled the industry, returns were slim at quarries whose rock restricted them to smaller and rougher slates. For instance, around 1805, when Duchesses were fetching £1·45 per ton, Ladies were only making £1.20 and Doubles a mere £0.78 per ton, and over the next few years the gap widened even further. As well as bigger sizes, the market was also demanding more choice, again favouring the larger producers. In 1788 Penrhyn offered 5 sizes in 2 qualities, by 1830 they listed 10 sizes in 3 qualities. This stock list was to progressively expand, until in 1880, 32 sizes each in various qualities were offered, even the humble Ton slates being available in 6 varieties.

In Meirionnydd, (mainly Blaenau) tonnage had gone from an insignificant 500 around the turn of the century to 12,000 by the early 1820s, mainly due to the export trade, boosted for instance, by the Boston city ordinance of 1816 that all roofs should be slate. This Blaenau tonnage would shortly look very small beer indeed, largely because of one Samuel Holland. A Liverpool slate merchant, his various enterprises, included pottery manufacture, quarrying on Cefn Du and elsewhere, and the merchanting of Penrhyn slate, (it was he who introduced Worthington to Penrhyn). In 1819 he speculated in a Take Note on Oakeley land at Rhiwbryfdir where, on the barren slopes at the head of Cwm Barlwyd, several abortive attempts had already been made to work slate. Holland's results being encouraging he took a lease, and in 1823 put his 19 year old son Samuel junior in charge of what would eventually become part of the great Oakeley quarry. The same year Bowydd was re-opened and copying Diffwys' underground methods and emulating their road construction, would in due time become a notable undertaking. As in other areas great technical improvements had been made in the larger quarries. Railed transport within the quarries was the norm, some mechanical sawing was being done and even trimming machines were being experimented with.

In Dyffryn Conwy, expansion was modest. Around 1830 something over 5000 tons was sent down river to Conwy each year. Some loaded at Tal y Cafn, but most from the two new quays at Trefriw capable of handling vessels of up to 50 tons. However it would soon become apparent that this was destined to remain a slate area of minor importance.

Meanwhile at Nantlle, fortunes were mixed, there being activity but little prosperity. Pen yr Orsedd and Dorothea (opened in 1820), both found the going tough and in 1825 Talysarn failed. The Cilgwyn Company languished, troubled by rock falls and the cost of additional leases, many taken just to keep competitors out. In 1819 they tried to sell, interestingly offered *'with iron railways, whimseys and cars'*. Their problems were compounded by Evans bringing in a friend, Poole, which caused friction with the other partners, and there were allegations and counter-allegations of fraud. Shares valued at £101 in 1824 were sold at under £4 eight years later, their once 2,500 ton output was down to under 900, by which time their 1816 workforce of 60 Bargainers and 40 Rubbishers, was more than halved, with their pay reportedly 9 months in arrears. Not that this was an isolated complaint, the 100 men at Hafodlas had similar problems and there were reports of them seizing loads of slate to sell them on their own account.

There were also at Nantlle, increasing difficulties of rubbish disposal, lack of space or lack of foresight resulted in mounds of waste piling up on top of areas of potential extraction. Such problems also occurred elsewhere, Cook quarry was by the mid 20s, putting out half of the 1000 tons it had been making 2 or 3 years before, yet nearby Glynrhonwy, operating on open ground was doing well in spite of transport costs, and in 1826 employed 126 men. Similarly other new openings with ample tipping space such as Ffridd and Bwlch Cwm Llan were successful.

For the Nantlle quarries road improvements had by 1811 largely cut out the Foryd transhipment, reducing their average transport costs from 11/- (55p) or more, per ton to 7/- (35p) or so, but each 2 or 3 workers in the quarry still required one man to cart. In the case of the cheaper slates which represented most of their output, carriage almost equalled wage costs[4].

The Penrhyn and Dinorwig tramways showed the way things had to go. However in Nantlle, diverse land ownership, and the practice of dividing holdings into many small leases, precluded the emergence of a dominant proprietor. In a spirit of co-operation, not always manifest in slate quarrying, a number of lessees agreed on the idea of a collective railway. Just a year after the Dinorwig line opened, the Nantlle Railway Company was formed, starting work in 1828. This was another notable event, as apart from its use not being confined to one quarry, it was intended for general traffic as well as slate, hence, it was, albeit horse-drawn, a full public and ultimately passenger carrying railway.

Unlike its two predecessors no great change of level was involved so inclines were not needed, and the negligible gradients enabled the use of trains of 2 ton wagons of 3'6" gauge. These wagons were unusual in having sheet-iron sides rather than being of the common crate like pattern, which enabled them to readily carry freight of all kinds. Uniquely for an external line double flanged wheels were used, which continued to be the practice up to closure.

The route necessitated a big, single arch bridge and a short tunnel (Extant at SH479600 & SH481616 respectively) as well as a bridge, now demolished, across the Seiont near Caernarfon. Much better constructed than the Dinorwig line it ultimately gave direct connection to the Caernarfon quay to almost every quarry of consequence in the area, and the endmost part of it remained in use, still horse drawn, until 1963.

Such tramways opened a widening gap between those that had them and those that did not, particularly if their product was not of the best. For instance, in 1820, Ddôl, could only obtain an average 18/- (90p) per ton at Wharf. Each ton cost them over 9/8 (48p), in wages to produce, loading cost 1/- (5p) and royalties 1/3½ (6.5p). Paying 6/- (30p) for carriage, left them no profit at all. Yet there were still new openings being made where the quality was mediocre and the transport prospects appalling, such as those around Cwm Croesor where at Brondanw Isaf, Brongarnedd, and even Cwm y Foel, handfuls of men struggled to produce a pathetic output.

As the largest employer, Dawkins-Pennant could also to an extent set the pace on wage rates which certainly failed to match the steep rise in slate prices during the early years of the century. Skilled men who might have got 1/6 (7.5p) per day in 1800 did find themselves getting around 2/6 (12.5p) a few years later, but the bad trade of 1814/15 soon forced pay down again. Wages rose a little in the brisk times of the mid 1820s but were back to near turn of the century levels in 1828 when Penrhyn laid off 100 men. This late '20s slackness, while not a recession did show the steam going out ·of the growth, which had brought Welsh tonnages of just over 20,000 in 1786, to five times that figure 40 years later.

This setback was largely because a great dead hand lay over the Welsh slate industry, the Slate Tax. Imposed in 1794 as a war-time measure, like other war-time measures before and since, it stayed in force long after any need for its imposition had passed. In spite of repeated and vigorous representations to Parliament, it remained in the 1820s, a charge on all slate carried coastwise.

The Tax did not of course affect the Dinbych quarries, but those at Llangynog still had a long cartage to the canal at Llanymynech, and the Glyn Ceiriog and Llangollen quarries were little better placed. Thus their transport costs offset any tax advantage. In any case the inland quarries were insignificant, compared with the Caernarfonshire and north Meirionnydd producers who were forced to make the taxed, coastwise shipments. Nantlle had its untaxed Irish trade, but with the economy there moving into depression, there was no growth in that market. In fact for the same reason the Irish quarries were looking towards the British market, some such as the Imperial Slate Company of Killaloe, boasting that being on the Shannon, their transport costs were less than those of north Wales. Though the Irish quarries would never prove a rival to Wales, European countries, such as Belgium were also trumpeting their wares, and this certainly presaged problems which would arise in years to come.

The big potential outlet was Lancashire whose population grew between 1800 and 1830 from 672,000 to 1,600,000 that of Liverpool alone rising from 77,000 to 165,000 in the same period. The small but threatening Leicestershire quarries, were reaching this market via the new canal network. More seriously the Tax did not affect the expanding Ulverston quarries in north Lancashire. Since the levy was on a Headport to Headport basis, they could slip their cargoes along the coast keeping within the incorporation of the joint Headport of Lancaster and Preston. From there it was a short canal trip to the rapidly expanding cotton towns.

Then in 1830, the building trade started to really take off nationwide, but demand for Welsh slate did not. Prices already 20% below their 1827 peak, eased further in 1831. Penalised by the Slate Tax, it seemed the quarries of Wales would lose out in the race to roof the new houses, factories and public buildings in the growing industrial cities of Britain.

[1] The early Penrhyn Cae Braich y Cafn workings were on a NE/SW line near the present main offices. By 1793 they comprised about 70 Bargains extending over about 500 yards.

[2] Turner clearly had intended to remain in the Blaenau area, as he set up a family vault in Llan Ffestiniog churchyard. Due to the move the only interment was a child who died in infancy.

[3] The self-acting inclines, to become so common in Welsh quarries, invariably had two tracks. A rope wound around a drum, usually on a horizontal axis, enabled the weight of a downgoing load on one track, to haul up empty waggons on the other track. Movement was controlled by a brake on the drum. More fully described in Chapter 3.

[4] Costs for Hafodlas (Nantlle) quarry for August 1809, all per Mille other than Rags which are per ton, (all decimalised).

	'Raising' (wages)	Cartage	Price
Duchesses	£1.75	£0.90	£5.25
Countesses	£1.25	£0.65	£3.15
Small ditto	£0.90	£0.55	£2.15
Large Ladies	£0.55	£0.50	£1.75
Small Ditto	£0.41	£0.375	£1.30
Doubles	£0.275	£0.25	£0.80
Rags	£0.55	£0.50	£1.50

(in 1800 Countesses would have fetched £2.00, Doubles £0.70)

3. The Great Leap Forward
1830s & 40s

A small, but to Wales, significant effect of the Napoleonic wars, was the interruption of the 'Grand Tours' of Europe. People of means had to seek adventure nearer home, many brave souls facing the rigours of a trip through Wales. Some such as Pennant, Bingley and Bennett when publishing accounts of their adventures made reference to slate quarrying. Thus helping to direct the attention of influential Englishmen, not only to the beauties of Wales, but also to the investment opportunities it afforded. With slate operations becoming more capital intensive, such investment was now being called for.

Between 1800 and 1813 the prices of the larger slates almost doubled. They fell sharply in the 1815 slump, but within a few years had risen to new heights. In 1820 Countesses were fetching £4 per mille and Best Duchesses up to £7, almost exactly twice the price twenty years earlier. Wages which accounted for 80% or 90% of production costs had increased little. This was an equation redolent of profit. Thus in spite of the Tax and the mid 1820s financial crisis, slate was attracting the attention of financiers, including heavyweights such as N.M. Rothschild.

In 1825, undeterred by his Royal Cambrian Company's lack of success at Moelwyn, Rothschild's Welsh Slate & Copper Mining Company, offered Holland £28,000 for Rhiwbryfdir quarry. With only a few years to run on the lease, it was an offer he could not refuse, but he wisely retained the as yet unworked land on the rest of his holding. Although the Welsh Slate Company (Copper Mining was dropped from their title) ultimately became spectacularly successful, for the first 15 years it suffered heavy losses and was notorious for the late payment of wages. Not that this was exceptional, undercapitalised quarries, with money tied up in stocks and in extended credit, continued to be weeks or even months in arrears with wages. In 1845, workers at Tyn y Weirglodd, desperate for recompense, even offered to take payment in slate. As late as 1906, when the Braich Goch Company ceased trading, a testimonial from the men to the directors made particular mention of the fact that wages had always been paid on time!

However, besides failing to pay wages, W.S.C. also failed to pay dividends and Rothschild was replaced by Lord Palmerston as chairman of the company. The slate tax now impinged not just on the fortunes of financiers, adventurers and remote landowners, but on those of His Majesty's Foreign Secretary. Hence, in 1831 the tax, for so long lobbied against, vanished from the Statute Book.

The effects were immediate, prices firmed, outputs leapt. Penrhyn's re-employment of the 100 men sacked four years before and the taking on of more to push their manning to 1500, was typical of the resurgence. By the early 1840s, with outputs almost double those of the 1820s, the great era of prosperity for the Welsh slate industry was under way.

The greatest growth was at Blaenau Ffestiniog. In the 1820s it was already a significant slate producing area, dominated by Diffwys's 6000 tonnages. By 1827 the aggressive Welsh Slate Company had doubled their quarry's output to 4000 tons, but much of this increase was business captured from Diffwys. After 1831 there were genuine expansion opportunities for all, particularly for the likes of young Samuel Holland. Shortly after selling out to Welsh Slate, he commenced a new quarry at Cesail on the hill above his old working. Landlord Oakeley having insisted that the lease be split, the ground between W.S.C. and Holland's new outfit was let to Nathaniel Mathew. (Confusingly, this digging was styled the Rhiwbryfdir Slate Company, an anomaly ultimately resolved by the use of the name Gloddfa Ganol or Middle Quarry.) In 1834 Bowydd was taken on by Edwin Shelton and John Whitehead Greaves who had been working Glynrhonwy Upper and Faenol. They put in an extensive internal tramway network with an output soon to nudge 6000 tons. Greaves would later make a great impact on the Blaenau scene. The same year Fotty quarry was opened alongside Bowydd, (with which it would eventually amalgamate).

Young Holland had made road improvements, easing the

journey to the Dwyryd at Maentwrog, but like all Blaenau product, his output still had to make the difficult, expensive and tide-dependent voyage down river. With Porthmadog having opened as a port in 1820, trans-shipment was less perilous than it had been when it was done at sea, but double handling and breakages were still involved. Romantic though it might appear in distant hindsight, the fleet of 50 or so little boats, carrying tiny cargoes down the tideway already belonged to a by-gone age. Cost and delays apart, with annual tonnages in the mid 1830s approaching 20,000 there was just not enough quay space on the river banks to stock and to load the boats.

In 1836 the much mooted and discussed Ffestiniog Railway opened, which gave direct rail access to Porthmadog, giving the Blaenau quarries the potential to compete on equal terms with Penrhyn, Dinorwig and Nantlle.

It was largely Holland's initiative that got construction moving. In his Memoirs he recounts how, stopping for lunch at Penygroes, on one of his regular trips to the bank at Caernarfon, he fell into conversation with Henry Archer, who was investigating the leasing of the Nantlle Railway. He persuaded Archer to abandon his Nantlle intentions and to plan a railway from Blaenau. There had been many proposals, various interested parties pressing for different routes, as well as vociferous opposition from the carters and boatmen. Curious was the lukewarm attitude of W.G. Oakeley. Oakeley undoubtedly was reluctant to back a plan which would wipe out his rents from his Dwyryd quays and threaten the revenues of the Ffestiniog Turnpike of which he was a trustee. Indeed when the FR. opened, the Trust's revenues were immediately halved and the quays gradually fell into disuse, but W.G.'s widow (he died in 1835) was to prosper handsomely on the enhanced royalties from the quarries and from sales of timber as the Porthmadog shipbuilding industry grew.

In spite of being in much more difficult terrain than previous slate tramways, a constant and moderate gradient allowed almost continuous running by gravity from Blaenau Ffestiniog, nearly to Porthmadog. The one interruption being a hump requiring two short inclines, the upgoing one waterwheel hauled, the downgoing one, self-acting, (obviated in 1842 by the Moelwyn tunnel). The horses which hauled back the empty waggons, made the downhill journey as passengers in dandy cars. Like the Nantlle line, it was a public railway, and would survive as such long after the slate traffic ceased.

It had been costing up to 15/ (75p) per ton to get slate to Porthmadog, now it could be carried for 6/ (30p). Holland was the first user of the FR., although W.S.C. was the first to have direct incline connection. Shortly afterwards Mathew's also put in an incline, but partly due to the carters and boatmen slashing their rates it was some years before all available traffic went down the FR. Cwmorthin quarry opened about 1810, seriously developing in the 1840s, built its own branch to the FR in 1850. This branch involved cuttings, embankments and two inclines and was, utility apart, a fine and attractive example of tramway engineering. Votty and Bowydd did not connect until 1854. Diffwys, possibly because they had to justify their expensive road and because of their different rail gauge, did not connect until 1865. In fact the siting of their 1845 Pant yr Ynn mill suggested that they then had no plans to use the FR. The expanding Rhiwbach and its neighbours sited east of the Manod mountain still had to cart for shipment on the Dwyryd, but did benefit from the reduced boating charges.

Besides the FR the Blaenau quarries got another great boost following the Hamburg fire of 1842. Nathaniel Mathew's enterprise in visiting the city almost before the smoke had cleared, not only ensured re-roofing in Blaenau quarries' material but also firmly established them in the European market.

The FR. made the Dinorwig arrangments look very poor indeed. T. Assheton-Smith's son, (Thomas junior) had succeeded his father in 1827 and when Turner left the following year to pursue his other interests, he took an active part in the quarry management. Deciding that the existing tramway would not do, he took radical steps to replace it. Some construction seems to have been made for a line some 300' above Llyn Padarn, but when the Padarn railway opened in 1842, it was almost at lake level obviating the uphaulage from which the old tramway had suffered. It tunnelled through the Glan-y-Bala rock and then ran alongside Llyn Padarn, some of it on the handy shelf made by decades of waste tipping. From there it followed an almost level cross-country route to the head of a big incline at Penscoins, near Port Dinorwig.

It was 4′ gauge, the reason for the wide gauge and the avoidance of gradients was that it was planned for locomotive haulage, and although for about 7 years horse-drawn, it was to be the first steam powered quarry railway, predating almost every other steam railway in Wales. The problem of mixed gauging was overcome by carrying the 2′ gauge quarry waggons, four at a time on transporter trucks to Penscoins, where they were lowered by the incline to the port. Although this incline was later to prove something of a handicap, the line served the quarry for almost a century and a quarter[1].

This, transportwise at least, put Dinorwig firmly ahead of rival Penrhyn, where in 1840 Dawkins-Pennant having died, the dynasty took a further twist. The heir was Colonel Charles Edward Douglas, who had had the wisdom to marry Dawkins-Pennant's daughter Juliana. He followed tradition by changing his name to Douglas-Pennant, and as a military man, began to run the quarry on regimental lines. Not perhaps the best model for dealing with sensitive 'labour relations' matters, but the army was then one of the few professions providing experience in the control of a large workforce.

Nantlle quarries had the benefit of their new railway, but expansion was slowed by their dependence on the Irish trade. This strong Nantlle-Ireland connection had in earlier years forced Penrhyn and Dinorwig to seek the then less remunerative outlets in England. Now with English building booming and the Irish depression becoming famine, the Nantle producers had the task of breaking into the English after its problems, managed to move ahead in the mid 1840s, commencing a 40 year period of growth that would put its annual tonnages near 8000. Dorothea, wavered for some years, but when in 1848 a consortium of local people took it over, it was to prosper mightily, until by the 1870s, it was turning out 15,000 tons per year, or around a third of the Nantlle area total. What was also to become another great Nantlle quarry, Pen yr Orsedd, was still not doing well, but by 1864 it would have 400 men and rival Dorothea. Besides these larger ones at Nantlle, there were many small developments on the south side of the valley. Some of which from the 1850s, had the benefit of rail connection via a branch line (The Caernarvonshire Slate Quarries Tramway).

Expansion was not confined to the north Caernarfonshire and Blaenau areas. North of Llangollen, the Oernant, Moel y Faen and Clogau quarries were growing and when in the late 1850s, they had a tramway (the Oernant) to the canal, they became quite significant producers. The Cambrian, in Glyn Ceiriog and some of its neighbours, were in spite of cartage costs, also picking up, as was Craig Rhiwarth at Llangynog.

In the South of Meirionnydd, at Corris, new road building allowed access to promising locations, and in the mid 1830s quarries such as Braich Goch, developed out of small, vernacular workings. Just as Cilgwyn men had migrated to Blaenau, three-quarters of a century before, Caernarfonshire men now came to Corris. But unlike the Cilgwyn men they no longer came as entrepreneurs, but as workers. This reflected the changing sources of capital within the industry. Up to this time, apart from a few landowners and big financiers, investors for the most part had either quarrying experience or some knowledge of the trade as local merchants or lawyers. Much of the Corris development was funded by investors of moderate substance, many from outside the area. As slate became more widely perceived as a source of profit, capital from such 'off territory' investors would became more usual.

As happened at Penrhyn and Dinorwig, the deep-pursed landowner could take the long view. Professional investors, with widely spread interests, could afford to wait for speculations to bear fruit. Businessmen, especially if they had experience of slate, understood the need to invest for the future. By contrast, the lay investor, perhaps lured by tales of untold wealth at Penrhyn, putting his savings into the latest quarry promotion, wanted immediate dividends. This short-term approach was to have profound and often disastrous effects on much of the industry. Good rock would be cast aside in favour of better rock, and sometimes badly framed wage-rates encouraged this. Rubble would be dumped on areas above good rock, so effectively constraining future development. Infrastructure would be skimped, collapses would occur due to lack of overburden clearance, or underground, to leaving insufficient pillaring. Profits which accrued in good times and which ought to have been retained for re-equipment or re-development, or as a nest-egg for hard times, were all too often disbursed as dividends.

Indeed in all fairness, if as was usually the case, a quarry was held on a lease of say, ten or twenty years, returns needed to be fairly immediate. Plant and machinery might ultimately be sold, but expenditure on buildings and civil work had to be recovered before it reverted to the landlord. Thus it was invariably only the freehold or very long-leased quarries which could contemplate big outlays on permanent structures.

The poor quality of managers was notorious, this often being due to a reluctance to put local men in charge. A man with scant knowledge, but who could be 'trusted', would be engaged rather than an 'unknown' no matter how great his experience and sound his record.

Unwisdom and incompetence apart, there was much outright fraud. A person finding himself the owner or lessee of a totally dud property would seek to unload it by floating a company and exhorting those *'Who were astute enough to avail themselves of a unique investment opportunity'*, to join him. His contribution was usually confined to making over the lease and the 'goodwill'. Invariably, the company would have 'agreed' to buy the plant and buildings for a generous sum and to have 'secured' his services as the (highly paid) Chairman or Managing Director. This 'pass the parcel', though less flagrant than it was in, say metal mining, was widespread and was to continue right into the 20thC. Such directors, having minimal equity themselves would, when it all fell apart, have no hesitation in putting the company into liquidation, buy back the assets at a knock-down price, and resume trading (or even float yet another company!). Prior to the Companies Act of 1862, this was, for the proverbial widows and orphans, very bad news, as subscribers were responsible for the whole of the debts, not just the amount of their investment. Wise but unscrupulous investors sometimes put shares in relatives' names. An instance of this was the Meirionethshire Slate Company which failed in 1848, with a heavy call on subscribers, several of whom denied all knowledge of the firm! The main promoter who had apparently transferred his holdings to his son and brother before the crash, picked up the plant and machinery at a bargain price and carried on trading under another name.

Companies with grand titles proliferated, promising the most optimistic returns from triflingly insignificant sites. The Prospectus would invariably include a report from an 'expert', who would declare it to be *an unrivalled opportunity*, the rock no matter how poor, would be pronounced *excellent*. If the term *Another Penrhyn* was not actually used, then there would invariably be a reference to *The great profits, now being made at Penrhyn*. Many were merely erroneous, but others were totally dishonest. Some did not actually own the quarries they offered, presumably hoping to obtain them if and when the flotation succeeded.

Not untypical was the Great Welsh Union Slate Company's abortive £250,000 flotation of 1857. The properties offered were: Hillsborough quarry (probably the small Corris quarry, Tŷ'n-y-Berth), Beaver Pool, an insignificant digging at Betws-y-coed, Tŷ'n-y-Ceunant, another small Corris working and 'St Winifred's' of unstated location. Two years later the Union Slate Company was more modestly, seeking £30,000 for Hillsborough and two tiny holes in Dyffryn Conwy, Penlan and Rowlin, which were such tiny scratchings that their locations are disputed. A year later the British Slate Company was looking for £75,000 for these latter two, plus Gaewern which though a bona-fide working was in difficulties. Research has failed to show that the promoters, some of whom were involved in all three offerings, had title to or options on, any of these quarries.

Financial juggling apart, there were still men trying to make honest livings, usually against the odds. The unsuccessful 1820s digging at Brondanw Isaf, has been mentioned. When just a few yards away at Brondanw Uchaf five optimists tried again in 1836, they were just as unsuccessful. They at least had a nearby road, but reaching Llyn Llagi called for a trek over bare mountain. Even worse placed was Arddu, halfway up Snowdon, where much of the product hacked out of a couple of holes, remains stacked to this day.

But in spite of error and fraud, the industry was moving forward. Although some small quarries stuck to their crowbars and wedges, increasing tonnages called for explosives, if only for tunnelling and for removing hard country rock. Some brave souls at Cilgwyn had used gunpowder to win rock since the end of the 17thC, and by 1800 limited use was made at Penrhyn, Dinorwig and elsewhere. The 1830 invention of the Bickford Safety Fuse, enabled shot firing to become standard practice. This obviated the somewhat fraught procedures described by Rev. W. Bingley at Parys Copper Mine in 1788.

'This process of blasting must frequently be attended with danger, as the men have been known to be so careless as not to be sufficiently distant when the explosion has taken place. The manner in which it was done was quite novel to me. They bore a hole in that part of the rock in which they wish to blast, about the width of a very wide gun barrel, and of a depth in proportion to the quantity to be thrown up. At the bottom of this they lodge their gunpowder, and then taking an iron rod, made about two feet in length, and tapered to quite a point, they place it in the hole, and fill it up on all sides with stones, clay etc. ramming it hard down with an iron, projecting at the bottom of which is made a nick, that it may pass freely round the rod. When it is filled up, and well hammered down, the rod is taken out, and a straw filled with gunpowder, substituted in its place. A match is then lighted and put to it with, as they express it, as much time in it as to permit them to get away, that is, of length sufficient before it burns through and lights the powder, to suffer them to escape out of the danger attendant upon the explosion'. (Until copper tampers came into use, sparks struck by iron ones were the cause of many premature explosions).

For blasting, shot holes skilfully positioned to move the maximum amount of rock with the minimum of damage (and least use of powder), were drilled with hammer and chisel or with a Jwmpah. This was a weighted iron rod upwards of 6' long, which by a repeated throwing action would produce a hole. Progression was 6"-12" per exhausting hour. Black powder was and still is, always used, as high explosive would shatter slate. Frightening though it now seems, in the early days gunpowder was bought from the nearest grocer!

The greatest developments were in what we now call 'materials handling'. Rail systems were being put in to move block within the quarry, to handle finished product and more importantly to dispose of the 10, 20 or more tons of waste generated for each ton of product made. Apart from development waste of country rock and overburden, this waste was mainly rock unsuitable for use and the offcuts from the dividing and squaring off of blocks. It all had to be taken away and tipped, hopefully on ground that would not be required for future working. Fine waste from hand trimming could be left where it lay, but with mechanical working, trimming waste and sawn ends would also require railed disposal. Even the smallest quarries usually had at least a length of track to a tipping point, or if underground, rails in the access tunnel. Eventually few workings were without rails of some kind, although Aber quarry, which produced slabs of 6' x 4' and more, relied on hand barrows right up to its 1920s closure.

Permanent rails in the more affluent quarries were chaired. Temporary sections and those in smaller quarries tended to be flat-bar rail tenoned into wooden sleepers. Slate in spite of its abundance was not very widely used for sleepers, and stone blocks were rare other than on the Nantlle Tramroad and initially, the Padarn Railway. Later patent metal track was widely employed, an early variety, popular in the 1850s & 60s, being the Thomas Hughes rail. This consisted of round iron bar 1" or so diameter, each length having turned down ends which slotted into cast-iron sleepers. It made a good, easily re-sited track, but unfortunately for Mr Hughes, the rails could be readily copied by any blacksmith, and a slab of slate, with four suitably positioned holes, made an excellent sleeper.

Waggons became standardised mainly into three patterns. Flat waggons with wooden cross-bars for carrying blocks. Iron bodied waggons open at one end for rubbish. Crate waggons for finished product. The wheels were often double-flanged, loose on the axle, to permit running on poor or makeshift track of variable gauge. Waggons were mostly hand-pushed, but for longer runs in the larger quarries horses or donkeys were used.

Blocks were loaded onto waggons by sheer legs. Underground, crab winches (which might be old sailing ship items) were used, lifting by reeving a cable through a pulley in the chamber roof. But even with good rail and lifting facilities, much of the 'materials handling' remained back-breaking work.

The layout of quarries tended to become more uniform as experience was gained, but scale, topography and the lie of the veins, meant that each one was different. Hillside workings might be worked on just the one level, but increasingly the terrace system pioneered by Penrhyn and Dinorwig, was used. In Cwm Pennant, little Dolgarth and its famously unsuccessful neighbours, Prince of Wales and Gorseddau as well as Arthog, Abercwmeiddaw and Cambergi would take this form. Later, before they went over to underground working, Penarth had a fine array of terraces. Early workings at Craig Rhiwarth, were terraced, but in a less orderly manner.

Other open-air quarries were pits. These might be hillside workings which had followed the slate veins downwards. As work progressed cuttings, then tunnels provided access and drainage. such as Cefn Du, Chwarel Fawr and several others nearby, developed in this way, as did parts of Dinorwig. Further south, the small and remote Gwanas and Darren quarries were to this pattern, as would be Maes y Gamfa, Golwern and many more. Cambrian (Glyn Ceiriog) eventually had a tunnel accessing and draining 4 pits, as well as serving underground workings. Abercwmeiddaw also had such a tunnel but its utility was limited as block emerging from it still had to be uphauled. Some quarries such as Pen yr

Orsedd, Braich Rhyd and Llwynpiod had tunnels solely for drainage, which, for various reasons such as emerging too far from the site, could not be used for material. Thus though they avoided pumping, they still had to uphaul. When parts of Penrhyn developed downwards an ambitious drainage tunnel was put in, but this later had to be supplemented by pumping. Rhos cut a tunnel which eliminated pumping and the uphauling of waste, but the projected new mill which would have enabled it also to handle good rock was never built. Llwyngwern had a tunnel, which had rail laid in it, but in the end was only used as a drain.

Pits in a valley floor like many at Nantlle had no possibility of a tunnel, so they had to be constantly pumped. In a few cases where there was a suitable water flow, self-acting injector pumps could be used, but powered pumps were usually required. Early ones were either rag and chain or bucket pumps but the standard pump, throughout the 19thC., was the lift pump, or in the case of deep pits, a series of lift pumps at perhaps 30' stages, operated by vertical rods. Water-wheel power was sometimes used, possibly with the wheel having to be sited some distance from the pump, Flat-Rods being used to convey motion. These rods, which could be several hundreds of yards in length, were supported by rollers, and moved to and fro by a crank on the water-wheel. Rhiwbach and Rhosydd, used this system as did Glanrafon where the rods ran along a drainage tunnel which further downward working had rendered redundant. A curious use of Flat-Rods was a pump at Graig Ddu, where a water-wheel lifted water not to drain, but to operate another (mill) water-wheel. Later, water-turbines were sometimes used to power pumps. In an endeavour to contain pumping costs, even wind power was experimented with (at Braich Rhyd in 1827). Hafodlas, as early as 1807 had put in a steam pump, the outlay for which continued to beggar them long after 1817 when it was wrecked by injudiciously excavating too close to it. Expensive though they were to buy and run, steam engines would ultimately prove to be the only solution to dewatering problems in many Nantlle workings.

Besides pumping, these pit workings required almost every

piece of rock, be it waste or usable material, to be up hauled. In the earliest days hand windlasses were used, some like Cilgwyn and Hafodlas uphauled by horsewhim, the latter keeping 16 horses for the purpose. (The only known surviving example of a horsewhim circle, where a horse walked around a vertical axle which had a winding drum at its top, is at Hendre quarry near Dolwyddelan). Where drainage was not a problem, water-balances[2] could be used, Tal y Sarn installing one of the first in 1829.

As well as water balances, water power was also used to directly crank uphaulage inclines as at Bryneglwys, Cefn Gam, Cymerau, Llechwedd, Moelfre and Rhos. The unique horizontal haulage at Rhosydd was also water-wheel powered. Some such as Gwernor used water-turbine haulage. Most of these uphaulages were on an inclined plane, but others, especially in the Nantlle pit workings, were chain-inclines. Instead of ascending on railed ramps, trucks hung from sheaves running on chain or rope catenaries. They were less efficient than conventional inclines, but having no fixed formation they could be moved as work progressed. A later refinement, used at Nantlle, Dinorwig and Penrhyn was the 'Blondin'. This consisted of a wire rope stretched between two towers either side of a pit. By means of a sheave running on this rope, loads could be lifted and transported to be landed at the edge of the pit. They were thus more versatile than the chain incline, as loads could be picked up from anywhere beneath the carrying rope, rather than the one fixed point of the chain incline, particularly useful where a pit was being worked in several galleries. These Blondins used two coaxial winding drums, one (with a single rope) for lifting, the other (with two ropes) to move the sheave to and fro. Operating the lifting drum on its own raised or lowered the load hook. With the two coupled together the sheave could be moved, with the load height kept constant. They were criticised as being slow, as being difficult to maintain (freeing a jammed sheave meant a man had to crawl out along the wire!) and though theoretically moveable, doing so was not easy. They were powered by steam, or later, electricity. In a few instances, such as

Hafod Las, Cae Abaty and Llwyngwern 'Scotch Derricks' were used to lift block from pits.

Fortunately, in most workings, materials movement was mainly downward, thus the double-acting balanced inclines pioneered in Penrhyn and Dinorwig proliferated. Upwards of 300 of these were built in the quarries and on the tramways of north Wales. The vast majority had a horizontal drum at the incline head, supported by two walls, joined by a roof. A downgoing load of one, two or three loaded wagons unwound a rope on one half of the drum, causing another rope to be coiled onto the other half of the drum which uphauled empty wagons. Great ingenuity was sometimes shown in raising heavy machinery by these inclines, exercises which were not always free of incident. Occasionally these inclines were single acting with a wheeled ballast acting as the counterbalance. In either case the operation was controlled by a brake, usually a strap acting on one end of the drum, operated with considerable skill by a brakeman via a long lever.

Normally the tracks passed straight through the drumhouse under the drum, but where space at the incline head was restricted, the drum might be remotely sited above and behind the top of the pitch. Sometimes where the head of the incline was on unstable ground, the drum was in a pit under the tracks, this was done at Dinorwig and at some Nantlle quarries. Most inclines had sprags at the top to prevent wagons prematurely descending, these could be anything from simple hinged bars to complex chocking mechanisms controlled by a lever handy for the brakeman.

The earliest drums were entirely of wood, but after about 1840, they consisted of a wrought iron axle, cast iron spiders and a skin of wooden staves, or very occasionally sheet metal. A few inclines had instead of a drum a single rope running round iron sheave-wheels on vertical spindles. These were common in the Corwen area, doubtless due to the influence of the nearby Wrexham collieries, where this sort of gear was commonly used. Such sheaves could be in housings or in pits below the rails.

In most cases the waggons ran on their own wheels, but sometimes, particularly on steep pitches, they were carried on tables or 'truncs'. Some of these table inclines were substantial pieces of engineering, carrying two or even four waggons, with complicated geared brakes to cope with the considerable loads. Those at Vivian quarry were particularly fine[3].

At first fibre ropes restricted incline lengths, enforcing several pitches on long descents as at Moelwyn, but after mid-century, wire ropes enabled single-pitches to drop 700' or more.

Where following the dip of the vein would involve moving excessive amounts of overburden, quarrying went underground giving rise to some of the most interesting working methods. Underground working became almost univeral around Blaenau Ffestiniog, and in Meirionnydd generally. In Caernarfonshire Tan y Bwlch and Moel Faban, were underground, as were many small workings. In Dinbych Cambrian, Wynne, Penarth, Moel Ferna and Cwmmaengwynedd, worked underground, and in south Wales, Penceulan.

Turner's 'cavern' style working at Clogwyn y Fuwch, was not repeated in Wales except tentatively at Aberllefenni. Neither was the Pen y Ffridd stone-mining method of extracting almost the whole of a near horizontal vein, just leaving pillars to support the roof. Sometimes a working was started by tunnelling straight into promising rock. It was more usual, having dug out an outcrop to drive a tunnel in from the hillside below it, and 'roof up' to the original hole. In either case, the extent and lie of the slate (if any!), and the amount of overburden was assessed and it was either developed as an open working, or the vein was followed by further tunnelling. This might be repeated higher or lower down a hillside, or if the find was substantial, worked by chambering as pioneered by Diffwys and Bowydd around 1820. This involved driving a tunnel across the vein, at right-angles to the dip of the vein, immediately below the overlying country rock. From this strike tunnel, sloping tunnels would be driven upwards, still just under the hard, at intervals of perhaps 80' or so. From these roofing shafts, rock would be extracted leftwards and downwards to create a chamber about 50' wide, leaving untouched a wall of slate (always referred to as a 'pillar'), perhaps 30' wide, to support the

53

ground above. Since this was usually repeated at vertical intervals, a chamber would eventually break through into the one above leaving a continuous sloping cavern. At Aberllefenni, in their near vertical veins, a downward variation of this method was used, which Sir Charles Foster, the Chief Inspector of Mines found sufficiently notable to publicise during the 1880s, in a descriptive paper.

Underground, pumping was required at least at lower levels, which usually called for steam (or later electric) power, although Llechwedd was able to use a waterwheel and Oakeley did manage to replace one steam pump with a water turbine. Occasionally drainage tunnels could be used, Rhiwbach having a particularly fine one, but usually the distances involved made them too costly. Rhosydd considered and Croesor attempted a tunnel and at Blaenau there was abortive talk of a tunnel to collectively de-water a number of workings, as was sometimes done in lead mining.

Underground working, in spite of the obvious difficulties, was often more productive than open working, as once the strike tunnels had been cut a minimum of non-slate material had to be removed, and block was always obtained from unweathered faces. Extraction could usually be planned so that working was basically upward and material removal downward. Also there were opportunities to minimise rubble cartage, by backfilling into worked out chambers.

Permanent lighting underground was non-existent until the 20thC. and was rare until recent years. An exception was the gas lighting installed by Holland in 1842 in his 1000 yard long tunnel cut to enable material from the main workings to be brought to the mill. Since this was called the 'Horse Tunnel', it was said that the lamps were for the convenience of the horses, not the men. Other than the carbide lamps carried by supervisors, the sole illumination was by candles, which like gunpowder and other consumables, were paid for by the men themselves. Sometimes they bought them privately as shown when a widow of a man killed at Oakeley in the 1890s asked for her £10 compensation as a lump sum rather than in 10 monthly instalments, as she wished to open a shop selling candles to the quarrymen. More usually they were issued by the quarry and deducted from wages, a remunerative exercise as instanced in 1877 when Braich Goch made enough profit on sales of powder, candles & fuse to cover their £200 royalty payment[4]. The sole later 'modern' refinement was the placing of candles into crude lanterns made out of one gallon oil tins, instead of just sticking them into a piece of clay. It was to be the 1950s before the Oldham electric cap-lamp completely ousted the candle.

Underground quarrying, particularly on a big scale, gave rise to much innovative engineering, especially in the transport of material. The horizontal tunnels, originally bored for access, formed ideal tramway routes. Where subsequent extraction interrupted these routes, bridges maintained continuity. These underground bridges were of up to about 50′ span, typically comprising two baulks of pitch pine, 18″ x 9″, decked with 9″ x 3″ timbers. Each baulk would have 2 iron bars 2″ diameter, projecting downwards a third of the way along. The bottoms of these bars would be joined by a 1″ tie rod and braced at each end by 1″ bars reaching to either end of the main baulks, where they were tensioned by nuts. Post and chain hand rails were usual. In the case of longer spans, chains from the roof gave extra support.

The dip of the veins provided obvious incline paths to link the different levels. Underground inclines were frequently of the table type usually with the wagons riding on a turntable (so that a long block coming in from a side tunnel could be turned to avoid fouling the walls of the incline tunnel). Also due to constrictions of tunnel width they were usually single acting, with the counterbalance weight running on a narrow track between the main rails. Intermediate tunnels crossed these inclines by hinged bridges. Due to lack of space, the head-gear usually comprised sheaves on horizontal spindles. Powered inclines for uphauling (unless in latter days steam or electrically driven), might, as on the surface, be water-wheel wound or water-balanced. Where a water-balanced incline operated below drainage level, the water tank might not run on a parallel track, but in an inclined or vertical shaft at a higher level, connected to the load by a rope led around pulleys. This layout was used at Rhosydd (before deepening of the workings enforced the use of a water turbine), and at Croesor.

To enable men to move between levels underground steps were sometimes provided, but commonly they had to scramble up and down hundreds of feet of waste, or use rickety iron or chain ladders to reach their workplaces. Not that those in open quarries were always better catered for. Pit workings, hundreds of feet deep, were accessed by wooden ladders. Extensive hillside workings might have steps which could be alongside inclines, or could zig-zag dizzily and possibly perilously to vast heights. At least men in open workings were spared the reaching of roofs of underground chambers to inspect for loose rock or to fix pulley mountings. Portable ladders 60' or more in length were used, which according to an early specification had to be *'British Larch grown on a plantation on a slope facing the north where the sun shines the least'*. They were leaned against a wire stretched across the chamber and their erection took as much skill as it did nerve to climb them.

Whether open or underground, rockmen all had the danger and discomfort of working high on a working face. They secured themselves by a rope (if underground, a chain) wrapped around one thigh. Although later when power-drills were used, men stood on planks resting on iron bars driven into the rock, rope or chain working persisted into the mid 20thC.

Whilst some of the techniques of winning and moving the slate, were improved upon in detail later, the broad principles had, by the late 1840s, been firmly established. The industry could look forward to further progress.

[1] The Padarn Railway remained in use until 1962. The only significant change being in 1870 when further tipping having provided a suitable platform, Gilfach Ddu became the terminus, to where the lower 'A' inclines were diverted. Product from the eastern districts was brought through the Glan y Bala tunnel by a quarry-gauge line. Later the line was re-laid around Glan y Bala on tipped rubbish. The abandoned tunnel becoming, successively, a workshop, a war-time munitions factory, and now a cable tunnel for the pumped-storage station. The only other changes made during the whole of its life was one slight realignment at the foot of the Faenol quarry incline, and the 1920s abandonment of the chain and underfloor-sheave arrangements at Penscoins and the substitution of a conventional drum and wire-rope. The section of trackbed alongside Llyn Padarn now carries a narrow-gauge tourist railway.

[2] Water Balances were vertical lifts where the weight of a filled water tank could uphaul a platform carrying loaded wagons. When emptied of water, it could itself be uphauled by the weight of the platform carrying empties. Penrhyn eventually had 7. (The headframe of one is preserved on site, another is at the National Museum of Wales, Cardiff.)

The same principle was applied for the water-balanced inclines, which were used at many quarries. The two examples extant are at Aberllefenni. Such an incline (for passengers) was installed in 1992 by the Centre for Alternative Technology, at Llwyngwern quarry.

[3] Table incline remains may be recognised by the pit at the lower end for the table and by the brake having some way of being secured.

[4] In the early 19thC. candles cost 1/ (5p) per pound, though this later dropped to about 7d (3p) per pound. Since up to 2lb would be required for a week's work, their cost loomed large in a man's budget.

4. Somewhere to Dig, Somewhere to Live
1850s & 60s

The apparently unlimited opportunities that quarrying offered from the 1830s onward, drew more and more entrants into the industry. Unfortunately by this time quarries were already established on most of the prime sites, resulting in much unwise investment at unproductive locations. With good luck, modest returns might be made provided that progress was cautious. However newcomers impatient to get into the big time and possibly to have fine buildings to impress backers, were liable to spend large sums on infrastructure, on new and unproved sites, exhausting their capital before, (or if ever!) any sales revenues came in.

An extreme example of this was the Gorseddau quarry of 1855. It was a most ambitious development, with terraces on 9 levels, planned so that extraction was done at one end of each terrace and dumping at the other. Interestingly, they seemed to have had both 2' and 3' gauge track on these terraces, the 2' for rubbish and the 3' connected via the incline to the line down to the magnificent cathredral-like Ynyspandy mill. This tramway, engineered to near main line standards continued to Porthmadog. No inclines were called for, the one short gradient being overcome by a reversing loop. It was certainly the best constructed of all the horse tramways. A village of some 40 pairs of 'semis' for the workers was planned, (although only 18 were completed) and Plas Llyn, the manager's house was of mansion proportions. Reputedly £50,000 was spent in 2 years. After 4 years work their 200 men could barely raise 1500 tons, which at 7.5 tons per man year must be an industry record for non-productivity. Their peak ouput of 2000 tons was probably less than half the figure needed to meet their wages bill alone. Incredibly they persevered right up to 1867, when their horses having been sold, their 25 tons of product was hand pushed down the tramway to Porthmadog. On the site it can be seen how they abandoned their neat, disciplined layout, generating vast mounds of rubbish as they desperately and randomly sought good rock, even at one point trying underground. The dearth of trimmings on the terraces and scarcity of sawn-ends on the mill-tip testifies to the smallness of the output.

Less spectacular, but equally typical was the 1859 Liverpool and Birkenhead Slate and Slab Quarry Co Ltd, whose name was a great deal more impressive than their quarry, Braich Ddu. With poor rock and even poorer transport prospects, they put in a mill and Hunter saw and somehow stumbled on with trifling output for over 20 years. Another quarry, Foel, high on Moel Siabod which had already proved a dud, was developed in the 1860s with a mill, 3 barracks and a multi-incline tramway. A second mill was put in at Pont Cyfyng at the foot of the tramway, which was soon in turn replaced by a third mill back at the quarry itself. More work was done on construction than there ever was on slate making.

Another example of the 'slate mania', again in the 1860s, was when the McConnels, finding their Lancashire cotton interests hit by the American civil war, took over a couple of diggings at Bryneglwys where the excellent rock had not been fully exploited due to transport constraints.

They built the Talyllyn Railway and within 5 years had 260 men at work producing up to 8000 tons p.a., a handsome output but not enough to justify the great amount of capital (circa £100,000) expended.

Whilst these are examples of funding coming on a big scale from afar, the impact of the local modest investor was growing. Although slate quarrying wages were minimal, they did in toto bring relatively large sums into what had been substantially a barter economy. This gave rise to an increasing middle class of small traders, many of whom put money into the industry. Directories were increasingly carrying entries such as *'William Williams, Harlech. Draper, Grocer and Slate Quarry Owner'* (1858). By mid-century such people had become more typical sources of capital than the larger investor.

These citizens often found that they had backed enterprises on doubtful rock calling for expensive cartage. Earnest promises of

'Jam tomorrow' persuaded them to meet cash-call after cash-call to pay wages and running costs. For year after year the outgoings might be thousands whilst the revenues were hundreds, until the patience (and the pockets) of the backers were exhausted. Invariably, there were other optimists ready to step in and pour in fresh funds. In fact it was commonly said that it was only the third owners of a quarry who ever made money out of it. An exaggeration of course, but since few quarries ever fully repaid their capital outlay, many did only succeed on the back of previous owners losses. Rhos for example eventually prospered in this way. Starting in the late 1850s, the third owners did well in the 1870s boom, and in fact it did well again in the inter-war years.

Whatever the source of funding, the best chance of success lay in opening in an area which a new rail route had rendered accessible, provided that unlike Bryneglwys or Gorseddau, the quarry was not burdened with its construction costs, (or operating losses!) This was the case when in 1859 the Corris, Machynlleth & Derwenlas Tramway enabled the quarrying around Corris to expand. Braich Goch, after a quarter century of falterings, became a substantial and profitable unit, eventually producing over 6000 tons p.a. with a workforce of around 200. Similarly Aberllefenni was at last able to get into the big time, eventually nearing 5000 tons per year. The tramway ensured the survival of Llwyngwern and encouraged new openings such as Abercorris and Abercwmeiddaw. Unfortunately, the Corris quarries were never able to provide the Corris Railway (as it became) with tonnages that would have enabled it to offer rates competitive with the much more heavily trafficked FR., so imposing on its quarry customers a slight but telling cost disadvantage.

By contrast, though the Montgomeryshire canal had since the early years of the century, provided the Llangynog quarries, with better transport than their old river Severn boatings, it still left them with the long haul to Llanymynech. In the early 1850s Craig Rhiwarth, tried to improve matters by using a traction engine but it damaged the roads so much that its use was banned. They had to temporarily lay off their 200 men whilst the horse and cart arrangements were re-instituted. Cwmaengwynedd later did use steam road haulage, but presumably their journeys were too infrequent to cause protests.

Rhosydd which had started as an open pit working in the 1830s, had an easy route down Cwm Orthin to the Ffestiniog Railway. Unfortunately this was classed as a bridlepath, and Cwmorthin quarry barred all wheeled vehicles from crossing their land, virtually isolating Rhosydd. The Croesor tramway of 1864 transformed Rhosydd's fortunes. It was a modest line, five miles long, dropping via three self-acting inclines, (Blaen y Cwm, Upper Parc and lower Parc), from the head of Cwm Croesor to the Glaslyn flood-plain and thence to Porthmadog. Though well constructed, it was not capable, nor was it called upon, to carry large tonnages. Entirely horse-drawn, (in later days locos did work to the foot of the lowest incline), it was virtually unstaffed, horses and drivers being hired as required. With minimal overheads, it was always able to undercut the FR's charges. It enabled Rhosydd to grow from an insignificant digging, to one of the largest underground workings outside Blaenau Ffestiniog proper, with by 1885, an annual tonnage of 6500 and over 200 men. Similarly the Croesor quarry itself, though not brought immediate success by the eponymous tramway, would, by the end of the century, under the great Moses Kellow's leadership, almost equal Rhosydd. Both these quarries were connected to the tramway by inclines, the whole of the over 700' fall of each being in spectacular single pitches.

The Croesor line also served other quarries. Pant Mawr's initial two-pitch incline link obviated a difficult pack-horse journey. When their workings progressed downwards to merge with Fronboeth the continued use of that incline would have involved uphaulage. To avoid this and to serve the small, open-air Cefn y Braich workings, a tunnel was bored in 1886, through to Cwm Croesor, the lower pitch of the original Pant Mawr incline being extended to connect with it. Unfortunately tonnages were never enough to justify the cost of this bold move. (Curiously, attempts were made to extract slate in the tunnel itself.) Parc quarry was also linked to the Croesor line, and a number of small, short-lived workings such as Croesor Bach, Llidiart yr Arian and the old Parc open quarry also used it. The remote Gelli, the tiny, improbably sited Cnicht (where a near vertical incline was attempted!) and the ephemeral Bryngelynen may have used the line briefly before giving up their struggles to survive.

Rhosydd and to a lesser extent Croesor were fortunate to just get into the good Blaenau veins. But nearby Moelwyn, revived in 1865 with a fine mill and excellent transport by way of an impressive cascade of inclines down to the FR. at Tanygrisiau, was just off the best of the rock and so its success was limited. Several small quarries close to estuaries put in their own tramways to shipping points. On the Mawddach, Arthog and Tyddyn Shieffre had such links, and on the Dyfi, Cwm Ebol and Fron Goch. This gave them efficient transport which to an extent offset indifferent rock, in spite of lacking the proper port facilities needed for the increasing size of vessels engaged in the coastwise trade.

The dozen diggings around Beddgelert, where in mid-century, nearly 100 men were occupied, were almost all unsuccessful, defeated by poor rock and lack of efficient transport. For years this area was canvassed as the place to be, since railway connection was 'imminent'. Schemes such as the Porthmadog, Beddgelert and South Snowdon Railway, with a planned extension along Nant Gwynant to Betws-y-coed, were mooted for decades. There would eventually be some formations constructed, but it was the 1930s before rail was ever laid. Most of these quarries never got beyond the hole in the ground stage, but Hafod y Llan, built a mill and put in a grand (and horrendously expensive) incline system from high up on the slopes of Snowdon in the confident expectation that they would be able to connect with the promised railway at Pont Bethania. The railway never came and they had to content themselves with carting from the foot of incline to Porthmadog. This cost them 12/6 (62.5p) per ton, twice the sea-freight to Liverpool and almost as much as shipping to the Baltic.

In Dyffryn Conwy, north of Betws-y-coed, in spite of indifferent rock, interest was renewed. At Cedryn and Cwm Eigiau, from the

1860s several companies successively invested heavily and a 5 mile tramway was put in to bring material out. The tramway had one short incline part-way along and a three-pitch incline down to the river at Dolgarrog, but rock quality apart, the use of the river was no longer an economic option. Though short-lived as a quarry tramway, the line was revived in the early 1900s, (in standard gauge on a slightly altered route,) to facilitate the building of Llyn Eigiau hydro-electric reservoir for Dolgarrog Aluminium Works. The 3 pitch incline being straightened into a single pitch haulage incline, which later also handled materials for the construction of the Cowlyd reservoir, via the specially built Cowlyd tramway. This tramway and incline, remained in use to service the reservoir until the 1970s. The incline formation also serves as a route for the hydro-electric feed-pipes.

Some better opportunities lay at in-fill sites such as Wrysgan, tucked up in a corner above Tanygrisiau. It operated for many years, its success only limited by the tightness of the site. Nearby, Nyth y Gigfran was less fortunate, the difficulties of working at such a ridiculous location compounded by legal problems proved insurmountable.

The one spectacularly successful infill site was Llechwedd. Greaves and Shelton, abandoned Bowydd in 1846 and took a lease from Lord Newborough of other land in Cwm Bowydd. Shelton died two years later, but Greaves, undoubtedly supported by his banker brother pressed ahead. In 1853 he extended onto Oakeley land, helping to boost the Oakeley royalty income, which by 1856 was £12,000, (and would double in the next 20 years). Having built an incline to the Ffestiniog Railway, Greaves shrewdly negotiated a cut-price rate to port of 3/3d (16p) per ton. (His robust attitude to the FR., and the threat of competitive lines being built, resulted in considerable subsequent reductions in the FR. rates). Llechwedd which covered all the best Blaenau veins, with few intrusions or discontinuities, was neatly separated from its W.S.C. and Votty neighbours by substantial faults. By diligence and innovation, he rapidly built it up into one of the great quarries of the Blaenau (or indeed any) area.

The pressure for sites, particularly around Blaenau, focused attention on quarries such as Cwt y Bugail, Blaen y Cwm, Bwlch y Slaters and Rhiwbach, which were hampered by their inability to reach the FR. From 1864, they were all able to make progress, when Rhiwbach built its tramway, and offered the others connection to it. The tolls thus generated were in later, harder times, to prove vital to the Rhiwbach company. This line virtually put paid to the boatings down the Dwyryd. In spite of the boatmen's charges being halved to 1/6 (7.5p) per ton, and the carters slashing their rates from 9/ (45p) to 3/ (15p) the only traffic which remained was a little from Cae'n y Coed and Braich Ddu, which by 1868 totalled a mere 8 tons. The 1869 railway bridge all but stopped navigation on the Dwyryd.

Generally, the new openings which succeeded were far outnumbered by those that failed. Some did prosper to a degree when prices were high, closing when the market fell, but most could not hold their own, even in the most favourable conditions. Many failures were due to trying to work rock that was not worth extracting, through having inconsistent split, irony content, fissures, faults, or any of the many defects that make slate rock uncommercial. Others were opened on occurrences that at first looked promising, but when worked proved to extend only a few yards, as can happen, for instance, when pressure inside an anticlinal fold produces good, but extremely localised metamorphosis.

Quarries continued to be opened where the rock was satisfactory but where transport was not. Some of these managed to survive, notably Cwm Machno where in 1854 a company set it out on its hundred year life. Not so Cefn Gam which produced exceptionally strong and flexible roofing material. At this remote site buildings were put up and machinery installed, but it was doomed by its long and difficult cartage.

Where rock was being worked that could not be finely split but was otherwise acceptable, there were growing opportunities in the slab market. Its uses for flooring were already recognised as an item in the Mining Journal for 25 April 1840 shows — '*Experiments have been made to ascertain the applicability of slate to other uses than the covering of houses. The result has been the discovery that, as a material for the paving of floors of warehouses, cellars, wash-houses, barns etc. where great strength and durability are required. It is far superior to any known material. In the extensive warehouses of the London docks, it has been used on a large scale. The stones forming several of the old floors having become broken and decayed, have been replaced with slate 2" thick, and one wooden floor which otherwise must have been relaid, has been cased with slate 2" thick, the whole having been found to answer very completely. The trucks used for removing the heaviest weights are worked with fewer hands. The slates being sawn and cemented closely together as they are laid down so they unite so perfectly that molasses, oil, turpentine, or other commodity which is spilt upon the floor is all saved; and as the slate is non-absorbent, is so easily cleaned and dries so soon, that a floor on which sugar in a moist condition has been spilled, may be ready for the reception of the most delicate goods in a few hours. Waggons or carts containing 4 or 5 tons of goods pass over trackways of 2" slate without making the slightest impression. In no one instance has it been found that a floor made of sawn slate has given way; in point of durability, therefore, it may be considered superior to every other commodity applied to such uses. The consequences of the discovery have been that fullest employment has been found in the quarries which produce the slates and that additional employment has been given to British shipping engaged in the coastal trade.*'

This together with the mid-century expansion in other non-roofing applications enabled a number of quarries to open on lack of split precluded the making of good roofing-slate. Slab production also revived some older quarries whose coarse roofing-slates could not compete with the thinner product which the market was now demanding. Slab workings had an advantage in that, generally, its customers were more interested in the price and quality of the product rather than in the perceived reputation of the source. Thus a new and unknown quarry or district could break into the slab market more readily than it could with roofing-slate. Success at Corris, the upper Dyfi valley and the Dee valley, was almost entirely due to slab output. Hafod Las, opened in 1854, with much money spent during subsequent years, was saved from oblivion by supplying slab when nearby Betws-y-coed expanded as a tourist centre.

Perhaps because it was a more prosaic, as well as a less valuable product than roofing slate, slab quarries were less subject to doubtful company promotions. Invariably when there was a questionable flotation of a quarry making both products, it was the roofing slate potential that was given prominence in the prospectus. Although a ton of slab sold for perhaps half the price of a ton of roofing slate, something like double the productivity could be achieved. If 'added value' items such as fireplaces, cisterns etc., were produced on site, even marginal quarries such as Maes y Gamfa and Ratgoed could be profitable. Later in the century, Parc with its Kellow's patent interlocking ridging and other specialities, would obtain an average of £4 per ton for its slab product, almost equal to the price of best roofing slate.

For whichever product, the quarries were drawing more and more men into employment increasing the demand for homes in the towns, villages and hamlets. Quarry owned housing at Penrhyn and Dinorwig (which had respectively, 1000 and 700 cottages), has been mentioned, but large-scale lettings by quarries was not a widespread Caernarfonshire practice. (Gorseddau's Treforus village of 80 would have very much been an exception). Rhos, Prince Llywelyn, Hafod Las and Cwm Machno had some, but apart from the Pen yr Orsedd housing, the Nantlle and Cefn Du quarries had very few. Thus most housing in the county was private, in the towns tending to be speculatively built for sale or more usually, to let. Some houses in places such as Llanberis being quite substantial, catering for the growing hierarchy of the big quarries.

Outside the towns owner-occupation, frequently self built, was more usual. Some in the chapel-centred hamlets, others in more remote locations, the owners often emulating their betters by the unauthorised occupation of Crown or common land, undoubtedly invoking the ancient 'right' of Tŷ Unnos. This tradition was that if a house was commenced after sunset and was roofed with a smoking chimney, before sunrise, right of occupancy was established, together with land '*an axe throw from the door*'. (It is of course unlikely that this ever had any legal basis and certainly not in recent centuries.)

The costs of building or buying homes were met through Building Societies. These societies, among the first in Britain, were numerous in all the slate towns. Few were 'permanent' Building Societies in the modern sense, most comprising groups of men clubbing together to finance each others dwellings, the society being wound up when all had been housed.

In Caernarfonshire settlements nucleated around a quarry were rare. An exception, was Rhiwddolion alongside the little Bwlch Gwyn quarry. After the quarry closed the community survived for many years, the men obtaining work at Blaenau. Although by then there were trains, a daily walk of several miles to Pont y Pant had to be made to catch it.

Most non-urban homes had at least some cultivatable ground, and town dwellers might grow say, potatoes or dig peat on a farmer's land in return for help at harvest time. Consequently most quarrymen expected to absent themselves from work when their, or a neighbour's holding needed attention, in accordance with the country tradition of exchange of labour. In north Caernarfonshire, even those with no stock or produce to deal in, invariably attended the quarterly Bangor Fair, to buy clothes and household durables. (This and the habit of buying from pedlars accounting for the paucity of shops in the area.) The practice of taking unofficial time off for agricultural purposes caused friction with managements right up to modern times[1].

Meirionnydd generally followed a different pattern. Most employment was concentrated around Blaenau Ffestiniog, where by mid-century its teeming rows of terraces, were bursting at the seams. Racked by epidemics, the provision of night-soil carts was considered the ultimate in municipal sanitation. Consequently, besides the one or two houses on site for 'on call' workers, such as smiths or enginemen, all the bigger quarries built and let large numbers of dwellings. Cwmorthin, for instance, having no fewer than 53 (and 3 chapels) some near the site, others at Tanygrisiau. Rhiwbach, in addition to its terrace in Cwm Penmachno had a complete 'village' at the quarry itself with a chapel which served as a school and 'community centre' during the week. There was also a small shop, but main purchases were made in Blaenau on a Saturday, the 'shopping' being carried up the tramway on Monday's rake of empty wagons. Almost all shops on quarry property were privately run. Except briefly at Dinorwig, Cilgwyn and W.S.C., there appear to have been no instances of the 'Company' shops which gave rise to discord in other industries. Rhosydd also had its own community, complete with the obligatory chapel. Even quarries as small as Foel Gron owned a few houses.

In the south of the county, much of Corris belonged to Braich Goch and Aberllefenni owned virtually the entire village, where hood mouldings and other architectural detail contrasted with the more basic design of many company houses elsewhere. Abergynolwyn was created out of two hamlets by the Bryneglwys quarry. Ratgoed's minuscule settlement had a shop, and chapel with a resident minister.

Further afield, most of the dispersed quarries such as Penarth and Moel y Faen, built cottages for their employees. In south Wales, Fforest quarry near Cardigan, had a self contained settlement, which, in spite of its isolation, outlasted the quarry by over 40 years.

Accommodation was also provided by the well known barracking system, which was a formalisation of the custom for men living at a great distance to sleep rough in quarry buildings. Barrackers would walk ten miles or more, early on a Monday, carrying their provisions for the week, and walk home on Saturday afternoon. The author recalls the late Mr Chris Evans of Dolwyddelan telling him how, when a child, Sunday evenings after chapel would be occupied ensuring that his father's clothes and provisions were in order. And how he would hear in the small hours of Monday mornings, his father creeping downstairs to start his 5 mile walk (in Winter in the dark, possibly in snow), over the mountain to Rhiwbach. Arduous though it was, this trip was easy compared with some Bethesda men's 10 mile walk, over a near 3000' trackless mountain to reach Cwm Eigiau. Barrackers paid 1/ (5p) or so per month to live in conditions which even by the standards of the time, were atrocious. Water for washing, drinking and cooking would be from a hopefully nearby stream which also served as a sewer for the lavatories (if any!). In the absence of a stream, barrackers had to buy water from enterprising pedlars.

There was a small barrack at Gorseddau and a larger one at Prince of Wales. Hendre Ddu (Porthmadog), Cedryn, Cwm Eigiau, Foel and Hafod y Llan, had barracks, as did the tiny workings at Cwm Bychan and Gelli (Graig Boeth). Dinorwig had quite extensive accommodation. However as with the provision of family housing, barracks were more common in Meirionnydd than Caernarfonshire. In addition to their tiny communities Cwmorthin, Rhiwbach, Ratgoed and Rhosydd had barracks[2]. Rhosydd barracks was one of the most notorious in the industry, draughty, flea-ridden and damp, men ate, cooked and slept, each in as little as 200 cu/ft of space (equivalent to over 30 people in a modern semi) at over 1600' asl. At Graig Ddu and Wrysgan conditions must have been equally inhospitable and Moelwyn barrackers (and possibly families also), existed, snowbound in winter, close to the 2000' level. They at least had purpose built accommodation. At Blaen y Cwm they had to make do with a disused smithy and at Graig Ddu an old mill.

Men working at isolated quarries such as Cefn Gam and Braich Ddu obviously needed to barrack, but such was the shortage of accommodation in Blaenau Ffestiniog that even the quarries close to the town had to provide barracks. Even so, many men still had to make their own arrangements. Some found lodgings (up to 14 being taken in some quite modest houses). Others had to sleep in stables and outbuildings in the town, (euphemistically called private barracks). Curiously, although Bryneglwys was no great distance from Abergynolwyn where most of the men lived, it had a barrack, older men being encouraged to use it to avoid the stiff climb to work each morning.

Sometimes the barrackers paid a woman 2/- (10p) or so per month to clean and at Cwt y Bugail, a family lived rent-free in exchange for the wife keeping the barracks in order, but usually the barrackers fended for themselves. Occasionally coal for heating and cooking was provided (at a charge!), but often they had to cut peat for a fire. In spite of the fearsome conditions, such barracks nurtured choirs and poetry writing, and some, such as Cwt y Bugail had a library and night-school. Where there was no other accommodation, lodging might be found on farms. Men who did so, usually helped out with the farm work, only going home on Tâl Mawr weekends, very much typifying the quarrymen's commitment to the land.

Barracking tapered off during the 1930s, the Dinorwig Anglesey barracks being ordered to close as being 'unfit for habitation' in 1936, a daily bus service being arranged for the 200 lodgers. The last barracks to be occupied was Rhiwbach, where in 1952 just two men remained. Both could have gone home at night, one lived in Blaenau, and the other was from further away but had a car. Presumably the barracking habit was after many generations too strong to break.

Even where there was no accommodation for the workers, there was invariably, even in the smallest workings, a house for the manager, sited where a full view of all comings and goings of the quarry could be had. They were often large and impressive, with 'mod-cons' such as an ice house for food storage, examples of which survive at Hafod Las and Cefn Gam. Unlike the workers' accommodation they were usually well away from the noise and dust of the working area, invariably closely screened by conifers, (which often still flourish long after the houses have been demolished). These trees gave privacy and dignity but as Arthur Jones, son of Edward Jones, the last manager of Votty & Bowydd to occupy 'Quarry Bank' recalls, made the house dark and gardening difficult.

Size apart, they all reflected the elevated status of the manager of even the smallest quarry, as for example tiny Ratgoed. Its manager's house though of modest size had its own convenience, whilst the rest of the population, including the minister, had to share one communal 'two-seater'. Such communal toilet blocks were quite usual in isolated quarry settlements, particularly where due to altitude or poor soil, houses had no gardens where individual 'Tai Bach' might be sited. The placing of these toilet blocks over a stream, meant that they were sometimes a daunting distance from the homes they served. This of course was hygienic as far as the users were concerned, but the same stream often continued on to be others' water supply!

[1] Official Caernarfonshire quarry holidays were: Christmas Day, Easter & Whit Mondays, and, unusually, Ascension Day. There were also half days on Good Friday and Christmas Eve. The Bangor Fair days became reluctantly recognised as at least semi-official holidays (unpaid, of course!)

[2] Both Rhiwbach and Rhosydd's original barracks were not the present ruins. The former first used an old farmhouse, the latter a building on floor 6.

One must, incidentally, avoid being too dogmatic as to which buildings were barracks and which family houses as the use often changed according to demand.

5. Mechanisation
Water & Steam

Early reduction of slate was obviously an entirely manual operation. Rough blocks extracted from the quarry face were converted into rectangles of suitable size by striking them with a big African-Oak mallet, or by skilful use of hammer and chisel, or later, by drilling a hole and judiciously tapping in the Plug and Feathers. Roofing slates were made by splitting along the plane of cleavage, with a broad-bladed chisel, then trimmed to final size and squareness with the Knife & Trammel. Slab was produced by splitting in a similar way, but was trimmed and squared off by the painstaking use of a stubby chisel.

Separation along the plane of cleavage presents no problems but for squaring off on the other two planes, sawing gives a better edge and produces a larger rectangle from a given size of block, especially for slab work. Although stone sawing was known to the Romans, gravestone evidence suggests that it was rare in Welsh slate working, until the 18thC. Early saws were hand-held framesaws with toothless blades up to 6'-8' long, cutting by introducing sand and water into the kerf. Such saws were still in use in some tiny quarries, such as Nantglyn and Berwyn, well into the 20thC. Faces sawn by this method can be recognised by the feint marks running along the length, with a ridge where the slab has been broken off to avoid having to saw the full thickness. (Sawing was invariably along the length of the cut, not across it as wooden plank is sawn).

The 19thC. expansion of the industry called for the mechanisation of sawing, which was probably first done in 1802 at a timber sawmill at Rhyd y Sarn, by driving a sandsaw by a crank turned by a water-wheel. Certainly by 1805 Penrhyn was sawing some of their slab product by this method. Such reciprocating saws gradually gained acceptance, at least for slab work, almost halving the cost of sawing. Power-sawn pieces are usually identifiable by the absence of any ridge on the sawn face. In spite of the development of more efficient circular saws, some reciprocating sand-saws remained in use for over a century. Tyn y Bryn and Deeside for instance, were still using them in the 1920s, and Moelfferna actually installed them as late as 1911. Shot saws which resemble a sandsaw, but use an indented blade and steel shot, widely used in stone quarries, were not adopted by the slate industry, but it is possible that one was used at Rhiwgoch in the early 20thC. Similarly multi-bladed gang saws, commonly used in the stone industry were rare in slate quarries. One was installed at Penarth in 1906, and a modern diamond bladed version is in use at Aberllefenni.

The first circular saws were hand cranked, the earliest known, dateable example of their use being the 1805 Suwsana Pierce gravestone in Llan Ffestiniog churchyard. Almost certainly cut in Diffwys quarry, it has on its edges the characteristic curved marks of a circular saw. Such saws found little favour with proprietors (and certainly none with those turning the cranks!), but did offer some advantage over frame saws where no power was available. Gaewern, had at least two such tables in the late 1840s, and Darren had one or two in the 1850s. Bron Goronwy and Gwanas had one each and Cwmmaengwynedd even had one underground. It presumably being cheaper to hack out an alcove than erect a building. Resulting lighting costs did not figure in the reckoning as the men paid for their own candles!

The great step forward in speeding up sawing was the use of powered circular saws. Diffwys experimented with a horsewhim powered one at Rhyd y Sarn in about 1815. It does not appear to have been a success and it was only after powered circular saws had been thoroughly developed for timber and stone during the 1820s that the slate producers took a serious interest in them. Bowydd was using them by 1830, with Penrhyn, Dinorwig and the larger Blaenau units installing them over the next ten years or so. Although some quarries, particularly those in Nantlle lagged in the adoption of this new technology, powered circular sawing was fairly general by the 1850s.

There were many saw patents issued, including that of 1855 for the fearsome Hunter saw, whose replaceable teeth predated the general use of such items in engineering by almost a hundred years. Like some other early types the blade moved over the block being sawn. But it was the Greaves pattern of 1850, or variations of it, became the industry standard. These had a moving table, with the toothed blade (revolving at about 30 rpm), protruding from underneath. On some, the table was advanced by a chain, but almost all had a rack driven by a double worm-gear train from the blade shaft. Although 2 & 3 speed devices were tried, normally the table feed rate could not be varied for different thicknesses and hardnesses of block. De Wintons did make one batch of saws for Pen yr Orsedd in the 1880s with hydraulic table feed. These, by exerting a constant pressure, rather than a constant rate of table travel gave automatic compensation for varying cutting conditions. Though apparently successful, hydraulic feed proved unpopular and fixed feed-rate saw tables remained in use up to the 1960s.

Since at first saws were used only for slab production, quarries which dealt with both roofing slates and slab, only sent block destined for slab work to the saw-mill, continuing to produce roofing-slate entirely by hand in open-fronted Gwaliau close to the quarrying face or adjacent to the adit. In a big quarry these dressing sheds would be numerous, arranged in rows of a dozen or more. (Although work in some small quarries was still being done without shelter of any kind.) Thus, whilst quarries dealing exclusively in roofing slates, might not have saws, ultimately scarcely any slab quarries were without them. Even very modest workings such as Hafoty and Cwmcaeth had their little mills with just one or two water-powered saws.

Some Blaenau quarries started to saw all product as early as the 1850s but this was not normal elsewhere until much later, particularly where the harder Cambrian rock was being worked. Penrhyn did not completely abandon hand working of roofing slate until 1912, when they installed 100 extra saws to do so.

Blocks for slab or for Writing Slates were sawn to rectangles of finished size before splitting. Some attempts were made to popularise roofing slates with such sawn edges (Mill Slates) but fashion demanded the chamfered edge which is produced on the underside of a slate when it is trimmed. So blocks for roofing slate were sawn slightly oversize and trimmed after splitting.

When power driven trimming machines were developed, it was logical to site them in the same building as the saws, giving rise to the largely Blaenau Ffestiniog inspired Integrated mill. The first such mill was probably Diffwys No.6 (circa 1860), trimming with massive guillotines, which had been pioneered at Mathew's in the early 1850s. Holland's at first used a trimmer of their own design but soon adopted the widely accepted Greaves rotative trimmer.

Typically, the Integrated mill was a long building, with a number of saws along the back wall, driven in pairs from line-shafting above. The line-shafting would also drive, by horizontal belts, slave pulleys to serve the trimmers which would be sited along the opposite wall. The machines were controlled by the usual 'fast and loose' pulley system. Occasionally the line-shaft was under the floor, either in a slab-covered trench as at Aberdunant and Hafod Las, or in a sort of cellar as at Cambergi and Ynysypandy. Either arrangement cleared the working area of belts, and relieved the building of stress-loads, but a trench could get jammed with sawing dust.

There exists from an unknown late 19thC. source a somewhat poetic description of an Integrated Mill, almost certainly at Blaenau.

'*The dressing shed and saw house was a long, lofty building, dull of light and air. Tramways ran into it from every side and conveyed the great blocks of raw slate to the millmen. Aloft, the beams of this workshop were whitewashed and a revolving rod from the giant steam engine of the works ran the length of the shed. Wheels spun from this rod at regular intervals and from them fell a system of endless bands to the machines beneath them. Some dropped to saw tables, some to the dressers sitting behind their guillotines. The main tramway separated these operations, and from time to time little tumbrils entered dragged by a horse. They brought fresh slate and removed the masses of splinters and debris. The air was misty with slate dust and through the haze whirled the endless straps, flashed the steel wheels from which they came and moved the drab figures of a hundred men and boys. The prevalent colour of the shed and all therein was blue/grey, dim on dull days, brightened from the glass roof on sunny ones. The golden light winnowed down through the dusty air, flashed on the faces of the saw-tables and struck brightly along the surfaces of the polished metal and the wet planes of the slate. Beside each saw-table stood the great masses of native rock as the men prepared them for the saw.'*

Mechanical trimmers were never universal in Caernarfonshire, the knife and trammel remaining in use until the 1960s, but where machines were used, they tended to be the Francis pattern. Invented by a manager at Penrhyn, they had swinging shears like a paper trimmer, and were considered more suitable for the brittler Cambrian rock than the Greaves machines. Like some versions of the Greaves, they could be treadle operated, and thus sited remote from a power source such as in a gwal. In later Caernarfonshire mills even where all trimming was done by hand, the layout tended to resemble the Blaenau Integrated mills, but in place of trimming machines, there might be alcoves where the hand-trimming was done.

There have been many attempts to devise a mechanical splitter, but it still remains a hand operation[1]. In an Integrated mill splitting was carried out in the space between the saws and the trimmers. The blocks which would usually be split to 2″-2½″ thick before sawing, were split to final thickness by halving and then halving the halves and so on. (Since modern diamond saws can make greater depths of cut, nowadays the initial splitting is done after sawing.)

An interesting feature of some larger mills was the arrangement for getting rid of the waste. Sawn ends, generally had to be hand-loaded into waggons, but several mills, particularly in Blaenau, had chutes to direct trimming waste into waggons on a track alongside and at a lower level than the mill. Croesor had rubbish waggons running below the mill floor itself, an arrangement that may have been intended at Ynysypandy. Rhiwbach had a tunnel under the mill for fine saw-waste. Attempts were made to use belt conveyors for the removal of mill-waste, but it is only in recent years that the problems of jamming and wear have been overcome.

With the sole exception of Ynysypandy, all mill buildings were single storey. In fact it was unusual for any quarry building, other than a dwelling to have an upper floor. Mills had few if any windows, depending for light on ever open doors (even in winter!), and skylights. The use of glass skylights vulnerable to debris from injudicious blasting accounts for the large stocks of glass which appeared on quarry inventories.

Mechanisation had a two-fold effect. The cost of plant and of structures to house them called for increased capital. It also physically separated the gangs. A bargain-gang would still work as such, the two senior men in the mill, with the other two or three extracting block which was sent to the mill chalk-marked to identify 'ownership'. But the differing working conditions tended to produce a demarcation. For instance, other than in the smaller quarries, the gang would no longer meet at mid-day in the same Caban or meal-room[2]. In spite of this physical separation, the 'gang' system persisted well into the 20thC. It was not until 1920 that Penrhyn adopted the modern system of paying rockmen for the good rock they sent to the mill, and the millmen for the rock they reduced, regardless of from whom it originated. At the time opponents of this practice alleged that the rockmen in the quarry would be less careful of the quality of rock they sent to the mill, if their remuneration was unaffected by its eventual out-turn. This had been proved to be untrue by Moses Kellow at both Parc and Croesor in the 1900s, where he claimed a 25% increase in productivity.

There were other and deadly results of mechanisation. Although any working of rock, particularly underground, can produce dust, mechanical sawing in the confines of a mill, greatly increased the incidence of pulmonary disease. And working with chill winds howling through the unheated sheds was scarcely less unhealthy than working in a snug gwal. Plus, of course, working with machinery coupled with the general increase in the pace of work it imposed, brought additional possibilities of accidents.

Mill machinery was not confined to saws and trimmers. Planers were used to smooth slab product, the earliest probably being the Hunter (patent 6794 of 1835) which was a massive double-acting, moving bridge machine, roughing on the forward stroke, finishing on the return. Later planers were invariably single-acting, moving table machines similar to those used in engineering. At first planed slab was a premium product, but by the 1880s almost all slab was planed, only the cheapest 'common flagging', being offered with riven surfaces.

Save for the tiniest workings, all quarrying called for buildings and with the increased scale of mechanised working these proliferated. Besides the gwaliau for slate dressing, there could be, particularly in Dinbych, also larger gwaliau near the mill where blocks for slab were split, and possibly other open-fronted sheds to store blocks under damp sacking to preserve or increase their moisture content whilst awaiting splitting. An office was inevitable and a powder house of some kind. This latter would be located out of harm's way, generally built with substantial walls but a flimsy roof (to direct any explosion upwards) and wood lined to keep the explosives dry. There might also be stables, fodder stores and sheds for holding fern for the packing of slates, and for other supplies. Except in the smallest partnership workings, there would be weighbridges to weigh rubbish to calculate Rubblers pay (and in some cases to satisfy a landlord's requirement to have dumped tonnage statistics). There would be one or more cabanau and certainly at least one smithy, where the most frequent job was tool sharpening, the cost being debited against the user's pay. (Occasionally smithing was a franchise operation, with a self-employed smith charging for his services.)

Machinery needed to be maintained. In a modest quarry this might just be a saw sharpening machine. Commonly these were automatic filing machines. Later machines, such as the Glaslyn Patent Sharpener, operated by a punching action, clipping an 'L' out of each tooth-root to re-form it, this enabled steel discs to be bought, costing perhaps £1 each, against the £1.50 of a toothed saw (mid 19thC. prices). A larger quarry might also have say, a drill and lathe in a corner of the mill, powered off the mill drive. The largest quarries had substantial engineering departments, the Gilfach Ddu workshops at Dinorwig, (which now houses the North Wales Quarrying Museum), being an outstanding example. It had 6 lathes, and other machine tools powered by an 85 hp Pelton wheel, which replaced a 50', 80hp water wheel. This also powered the foundry and smithy blowers, as well as the timber saw-mill. Other than steel castings, every quarry requirement could be produced on site. There was even a tinsmith occupied full-time in the making and repair of the canisters in which men's pay was put up. Penrhyn had a similar complex at Coed y Parc, powered by two inverted siphon-fed water-wheels. Most ambitious work could be carried out in these shops, making them independent of outside resources. It is believed that even saw tables may have been made, 'pirating' proprietary machines as patterns. The great Pen y Bont viaduct of 1854 was built by the Welsh Slate company's own carpenters, probably copying the viaducts which Brunel was erecting at the time.

Later structures would include engine houses, loco sheds and coal and oil stores. Later still there would be compressor houses and electricity plants and sub-stations.

If buildings were erected after sawing was commenced, they would usually be made from sawn-end waste, otherwise country rock, often in huge sizes was used. Whatever the material, they were frequently much more ornate than mere utility required. Even when they were devoid of the sort of elaborate embellishment as in the Hafod Las mill or the Vivian drumhouses, they frequently showed an elegance which reflected great skill and pride of workmanship.

Further buildings and machinery might be required if specialities such as mantel sets or ridging were produced on site. Several quarries, such as Bryneglwys, Penrhyn and Votty & Bowydd, had writing slate factories, equipped to both saw the slate and make the wooden frames. Several, most famously Penrhyn, set up crushers to produce slate dust, some of which might be utilised on site, as was the case at their Ogwen Brick and Tile factory at Coed y Parc.

A number of factories making these downstream products, were off-site and independently owned, (as was at first the saw mill at Rhyd y Sarn). Typically they started as a merchant installing a saw at his yard, to cut to customers' requirements slab bought in random sizes, later moving into more elaborate work. Richard Williams of Porthmadog, being a notable example, others being Owen at Blaenau and J.J. Riley at Blaenau and Deganwy. Williams' Eureka works at Port Penrhyn, Dixon's of Bangor and Fletcher's of Caernarfon were manufacturers of some substance.

Other works were sited to utilise a particular quarry's rail route. The Clwt y Bont Writing Slate works was on the original Dinorwig tramway, later the Crawia Slate Works was a complex of manufactories sited between the Padarn Railway (to bring in block from Dinorwig) and the Llanberis branch railway (to send product out). The Matthews' enamelling mill on the Corris Railway was a similar tied establishment. Inigo Jones works at Groeslon was set up on the Nantlle tramway to make writing slates from Nantlle material. When they went over to enamelling, the local slate proved unsuitable and they had to source elsewhere, successively buying Cae'r Defaid and Cymerau quarries. This works still operates as a fine finishing plant for Aberllefenni, still having a sand and water polisher said to produce better finishes than modern diamond buffing machines.

The stove enamelling of slate became from about 1850, a considerable industry. Fire-places were favourite, but a wide variety of items were so treated. Dipping, brushing, or later spraying, was fairly straightforward but the pre-heating and baking was a skilled process, calling for slab which would withstand the thermal shock involved. A few quarries such as Braich Goch and Hafod Las enamelled, but usually it was done by independent specialists.

Later, the buying or leasing of quarries by merchants became quite usual. J.J. Riley acquired Hafod Las and Rhos, and Carters the Liverpool merchants, acquired an interest in quarries in

Penmachno. In mid-Wales, Ellis & Owen of Aberystwyth leased Glandyfi quarry. Later the north of England firm of Hall, Harber & Thorne worked Llwyngwern and the Towyn company became interested in a number of quarries to the eventual exclusion of their original merchanting and enamelling business. The present ownership of Aberllefenni has a similar derivation.

Another result of mechanisation in relatively remote regions, was the growth of engineering works and foundries to support it. The most notable being Thomas & De Winton (later De Winton) at Caernarfon, who in addition to their well known locomotives, made various items of quarry machinery. Also at Caernarfon was H. Owen & Son, makers of saws etc. At Bangor was John Owen, at Tanygrisiau, William Lewis and at Aberystwyth, Greens. At Porthmadog there were foundries and machinery makers such as Griffith Owen, (later Owen, Isaac & Owen) J.H. Williams and Richard Jones. Ultimately to become the domiant machinery maker, was Turner Bros. of Newtown (Powys), who when the local woollen customers folded, made the transition to saws, planers etc. for the slate industry. Since the Welsh slate industry was the leader in mechanical innovation, these firms besides supplying quarries elsewhere in the UK, also sold in export markets such as Germany.

The intensification of working through mechanisation increased the demand for other consumables, leading to their local manufacture. A prominent example being Cooke's gunpowder works at Penrhyndeudraeth. Mechanical working also demanded the local availability of engineering sundries such as saw-blades, belting and lubricants, firms such as Celtic of Caernarfon setting up to meet this need.

Almost all machinery was driven by water-wheel. Normally of cast-iron with wooden buckets, driving line-shafting via a ring-gear, they could be upwards of 50' in diameter. Revolving at 3-4 rpm, some produced over 50 hp, and were usually of the more efficient overshot type. Occasionally they were actually inside a building as were the wheels for the Coed y Parc workshops and the Clwt y Bont factory. For mill drives they were normally on an end wall, but a big mill would be divided into two with the wheel in the middle, to reduce shaft length. Mills were sited with considerable care to make the best use of water. Sometimes this meant the mill was quite a distance from the quarry, as at Deeside, Gorseddau and Graig Ddu. Penarth and Foel also had supplementary mills remotely sited. Where there were several mills close together, the tailrace of one could feed others sited further downhill. Votty & Bowydd had 3 big integrated mills tandemed in this way. Usually a wheel had its axle a few feet above ground, with the lower part housed in an excavated pit, and possibly with the upper part screened to prevent the wind snatching water from the buckets. Where there was a lack of head of water the wheel would have to be sited at a lower level, driving by belt. Abercwmeiddaw, Cambergi, Cwm Ebol and Penrhyngwyn achieved this by taking advantage of steeply sloping ground, but at Maes y Gamfa deep excavation was required. The Ynysypandy mill had the water-wheel in a basement. A mill at Graig Ddu, had its wheel completely hidden below surface level. This was not achieved by actual excavation, but by accumulating rubbish around a pre-constructed wheel chamber, the mill being built on the flattened top of the resultant waste heap. This in-fill method was also used for conventional wheel-pits. Both at Rhos and Rhosydd unused wheel-pit walls may be seen on tips which were never filled to their intended height.

Occasionally, the mill wheel did a double duty, such as at Hafod Las, where a mill had been built abutting the self-acting exit incline. When the pit deepened to below mill level, a gear-train and clutch from the mill line-shaft was used to power the incline drum. This enabled it to act as a powered incline for lifting block to mill level, but still allowing it to perform as a self-acting incline for the dispatch of finished product. Aberdunant and Votty & Bowydd both had haulage inclines powered by extensions of mill line-shafts. Abercwmeiddaw also may have had a haulage powered by the mill-wheel.

Water turbines[3] being primarily constant speed, constant load machines operating at high revs., were not often used for mill drives. Despite this, turbines drove mills at Cymerau, Foel, Ratgoed and Gwernor (where besides driving 3 saws, also hauled and pumped). Hendre Ddu (Porthmadog), had a turbine which, after closure, it is said, earned some boys 10/- (50p) for helping it 'find its way' to a nearby farm to drive an electric generator. Some were retrofitted to replace an inadequate water-wheel, as at Gilfach Ddu workshops, at Hafod Las mill and at Cwmorthin's London mill.

Apart from later use for electric generation, turbine power was most often used for air-compressors. These came into use around 1890, enabling power-drilling to replace the chisel and the Jwmpah, which apart from some occasional use from the 1850s of hand cranked drills such as the Dixon, had been the only way of producing shot-holes. Besides drilling, compressed-air was also used to run winches, sometimes purpose-built units, but often adaptations of old marine steam donkey engines. Aberllefenni put in a fine turbine installation in 1897, which involved the rebuilding of the old Cambergi reservoir. Penrhyn put in a 350 hp unit to power a compressor in 1912, by which time many other quarries, such as Penmachno had similar but smaller installations. Croesor put in an elaborate hydro-compressor layout solely to serve an abortive development scheme. Unusually, at Rhos the compressor was driven by a large water-wheel fed by the mill tail-race. Actually by the time compressed-air was generally adopted, oil-engines were becoming available, so they were a common source of compressor power, which often led to their use for other purposes.

Whether for wheel or turbine, great ingenuity was shown in obtaining a supply of water. Obviously a dam was needed to store it, invariably of three-ply construction (two stone walls with clay between), but Rhos used slate slabs and one of Rhosydd's many dams was of timber. Worked out pits were used as reservoirs, as at Rhiwbach and Cambrian at Glyn Ceiriog. At Rhosydd and at Penarth abandoned chambers were employed. Often extensive leats directed catchment to the reservoirs, often several miles long. Further leats, frequently lined and covered with slate slabs, brought it to the wheels, the last few yards usually being by wooden launders on stone pillars. Turbines required a piped supply to maintain delivery pressure.

Following closure, quarry reservoirs or even the quarries themselves were frequently used for public water supply, or occasionally for hydro-electric generation, as at Moelfre for a farm and at Cletwr for Pale House.

Although by the time powered working became general, steam engines were readily available, they were if possible avoided, particularly for mill drives. Capital cost apart, an engineman was required, (who had to be at work early enough to raise steam for quarry start time). Consumption of coal, which at quarry could be treble its pit-head price, was heavy, as a mill-engine boiler had to be large enough to continuously drive all the machines, which meant almost as much fuel was used when only one or two were operating for part of the day, as when all the machines were operating flat-out.

Since there was at Blaenau such intensive work with limited water-catchment, particularly on the western side, steam had to be widely used. Welsh Slate at Rhiwbryfdir and Mathews' used steam for mill drive as early as the 1850s. Diffwys managed at first to use water by building a mill off site at Pant yr Ynn, but subsequent on-site mills had to be steam driven and by 1873 they were using steam for all power. Those with access to more abundant water such as Maenofferen, Llechwedd, Votty & Bowydd and Graig Ddu made maximum use of it.

Fortunately for many small mechanised quarries, such as Cwm Brechiau and Rhaeadr, they worked exposures in narrow valleys where a stream provided enough power for their modest needs, but for those lacking water catchment, such as Minllyn, Portreuddyn, (both early users of steam), Frongoch and little Cae Madog, with its 2 saws and 2 planers, steam must have been a burden. Tan y Bwlch had a 80hp, multi-purpose engine capable of devouring up to 5 tons of coal per week. A large slice of their gross revenue must have been required to pay the coal bill.

At Nantlle and on Cefn Du, as at Blaenau, there was intensive working with limited water, so many quarries had to use steam for mill driving, (as well as hauling and pumping). Although they paid less for their coal than some remoter quarries, fuel costs loomed large in their budgets.

For haulage, steam could be a proposition as its intermittent operation, might allow a very small boiler and firebox to be used. For pumping, steam in spite of the fuel and labour costs of 24 hour working, reliability and flexibility of siting could make it acceptable. Thus any quarry with restricted water supply used it primarily for the mill drive. For instance, Llechwedd's first steam engine, in the 1850s was solely for incline haulage, and in 1864 Dorothea's 3 steam engines were for haulage, their 3 water-wheels for pumping and mill drive. Cwmorthin used steam for haulage and pumping but water for the mills. Croesor, before electrification, used steam for pumping, haulage and unusually, for ventilation[4], but only as a stand-by in times of water shortage for mill drive. Some having used steam for mill drive, reverted to water. Rhosydd powered their No 2 mill of 1855 by steam, but although they continued to use it for pumping, subsequent mills were water-powered. Similarly Prince Llywelyn's 1850 mill was steam driven but by the mid 1860s this had been converted to water-wheel drive and the new mill they built in the 90s was water-turbine powered. Even in the 20thC., with oil engines, and possibly electricity available, water power for mill drive was clung to.

The larger steam engines were invariably horizontal units, usually with a separate boiler house alongside. The one big engine would sometimes do several duties, as at Rhiwbach where the same engine powered the mill, uphauled to it and powered the exit incline. Interestingly, the similarly laid out Blaen y Cwm used their engine for both their inclines, but only as a stand by for the mill. Towards the end of the 19thC. 'portable' engines were available as standard catalogue items. These self-contained engines were based on a standard traction engine fire-box/boiler unit with cylinders mounted either above or below the boiler. They were handy as a main drive in smaller quarries, or as readily moveable power-sources in larger ones. At Cwt y Bugail, such a unit was used for a rubbish uphaulage.

Because of the dearth of fast-flowing streams and the proximity of collieries, some very small south Wales quarries, such as Sealyham used steam. Abereiddy used it for uphaulage, Porthgain had steam engines for haulage and mill drive. Trwynllwyd and Llwynpiod both hauled block up to the mill from winches driven by the mill steam engine. Glogue had a steam mill, and Dolbadau and Fforest somewhat unusually used steam cranes.

Ephemeral uses of steam included drilling and for boring machines, which were tried out for the cutting of tunnels. There was some success at Maenofferen, (where the partly machine-cut Cooke's level is still in use), but at Abercwmeiddaw, it was a failure and their borer remained on site, unused for many years.

Finally it must be said that although the Welsh quarry industry has been criticised for its lack of efficiency and its reluctance to modernise, there can be few industries, certainly none so remotely sited, which have so consistently displayed so much engineering ingenuity and innovation, in the face of extreme financial constraints.

[1] Over the years there were frequent reports from abroad of successful mechanical splitting. In the 1970s Llechwedd imported a French machine and Penrhyn commissioned the development and installation of several. Success was very limited.

[2] The caban was much more than just a place where meal-breaks were taken, it was the focus of a fervent mutual loyalty. After eating, programmes of study, debate, self-education, or (extending perhaps over several weeks) an Eisteddfod was held, presided over by the elected chairman. When the author had the honour of being a guest in a Caban, he found the rigid etiquette, more appropriate to the most formal of banquets than to a scratch snack in the barest of surroundings.

[3] Strictly the 'turbines' were usually Pelton wheels which are driven by a nozzle impinging on buckets. Turbines are axial flow devices, which require less head but need more flow than Peltons, thus were unsuitable for sparse, fast flowing mountain streams.

[4] In spite of the smoke and dust of blasting, and even, as at Cwmorthin steam engines being used underground, forced ventilation was extremely rare. Cwmmaengwynedd had a water-wheel driving a fan, and Maenofferen now uses electric fans, but even the use of doors to direct natural air circulation underground was never common. When compressed air drills etc. came into use, these of course helped to bring fresh air into the workings.

6 Ships and Trains
By Sea and by rail

There is in Wales, particularly in the north-west, a long maritime tradition. Responding to the expansion of the slate trade, shipbuilding, seafaring and their attendant occupations became a substantial industry whose fortunes intertwined with those of the quarries. It brought prosperity to such ports as Caernarfon, Aberdyfi and Barmouth besides creating Port Dinorwig, Port Penrhyn and greatest of all, Porthmadog.

Brigs, brigantines, barques, barquentines and schooners of all kinds were built by the hundred at the ports and creeks of Gwynedd. The 8 yards at Porthmadog and Borth y Gest alone built over 260 ships of from 30 to 40 tons between 1826 and 1913. These little ships, some manned by as few as 4 local men and boys, were willing and able to sail to any part of the world.

Oak for framing was selected by the shipwrights from the standing trees of nearby estates, but planking called for pitch pine and timber merchants set up to import it. Block makers, repairers, chandlers and so on flourished. Foundries in addition to supplying the quarries made ships fittings. Retired Captains or in some cases their womenfolk, taught navigation.

A number of ships belonged to quarries, the Cefn Ddu company had one early in the 19thC and not long afterwards Samuel Holland had his own ship. In time many quarries and merchants had their own vessels, some such as Penrhyn, Dinorwig and Llechwedd had fleets. But the majority were independently owned, title being divided into sixty-fourth shares, typically a number being held by the master with the rest split between local tradesmen, shopkeepers, farmers, possibly ministers and even quarrymen. The sums involved were not necessarily great, as in spite of their sturdy, close-framed construction, builders charged little more than £10 per ton, and old but sound vessels were available for a fraction of this. With luck, returns could be good, but given the hazards of any maritime venture, risks were great. To minimise and spread these, owners clubbed together forming Insurance Societies[1].

The seamen certainly suffered as much discomfort and danger as the quarrymen. Dangerous though quarry work was, (Penrhyn, by no means the most perilous quarry, recorded 258 fatalities between 1826 and 1875), the risk to life in a small sailing ship was even greater. Apart from deaths from falls and accidents or being lost overboard, most vessels eventually sank usually with all hands. Plus there were diseases caught in foreign ports and illness from living in wet clothes for weeks on end. Both crews and owners also shared the economic hazards of the industry, for when demand dropped, freight rates fell and vessels and seamen were idle.

Cargoes were not confined to slate. The agriculture of north-west Wales, poor though it was, produced some surpluses. Livestock could be driven to market but things like dairy products could not. The growth of regular sailings enabled such items as butter from south Caernarfonshire to be sold in London, which by the 1820s was a regular trade. The inbound traffic was just as beneficial as hitherto scarce commodities like flour, could readily come in as return cargo. Some owners such as Holland regularly brought in provision shipments, partly for profit, partly with welfare in mind. On at least one occasion, at a time of slack trade Assheton-Smith brought in a cargo of grain to be sold at cost to necessitous quarrymen. Local agriculture also gained as fertiliser such as superphosphate could be readily brought in.

The great railway boom of the mid 1840s brought no trains to Wales, but it did create a new market for slate to roof the stations, the sheds and the new railway towns, reversing the slackness which had set in at the start of the decade. This initial boom was checked by financial uncertainties in 1848, but in the 1850s, took off again with renewed vigour, fuelling slate demand not only for the railways' own needs but also from the much greater demands created by the newfound national prosperity of the railway age. The quarries and slate ports flourished.

This 1850s rail building did bring railways to Wales, initially just along the north and south coasts, but expanding over the next 20 years into a comprehensive network. Their actual construction had little impact. In spite of the large number of men required for railway building, few slate workers seem to have been attracted by the comparatively high wages offered. Similarly, for obvious reasons, railway construction workers showed no anxiety to stay on and seek work in the slate quarries. There were however some instances of railway entrepreneurs investing in slate, Thomas Savin being a founder director of the Diffwys Casson Slate Quarry Company of 1863. However once built the effect of the railways was immense.

No longer did quarries or their customers have to be within reach of a seaport or canal, they could be almost anywhere. By the mid 1860s, small quarries to the south of the Mawddach estuary, such as Henddol, Golwern and Bryngwyn could develop, carting their few hundred tons of product to the Cambrian Railways line. As could other quarries on the coast such as Tyn y Coed and Ffridd Olchfa. Llanfair could abandon their loadings onto little boats and Tyddyn Shieffre could divert its tramway to the railway. Paradoxically, when in 1868, Arthog quarry replaced their tramway to the river with an incline to the railway, and built a nice new mill to handle the expected extra throughput, they closed within a year. Cwm Ebol could now use the railway but oddly Fron Goch with the railway passing its door, does not seem to have done so. The Cambrian line from 1867, also provided an outlet for Minllyn quarry, via the private standard gauge Mawddwy branch, which in turn, enabled the Hendre Ddu tramway to be built to serve Hendre Ddu, Maes y Gamfa, Gartheiniog, and other small slab workings in the Angell valley.

By 1860 the G.W.R. Dolgellau line enabled such workings as Deeside, Moelfferna, Penarth, Cletwr (Pale), to really get into business, and being nearer to inland markets, to even have a slight competitive edge over rail borne loads from further west.

Deeside and Moelfferna were connected to the railway at Glyndyfrdwy by a tramway. This line, built in 1871 shortly after the Deeside quarry opened, apart from being to the unusual gauge of 2'7", astonishingly, had wooden rails (sheathed with iron

Such strapways had been dearer than iron rails since the fall of iron prices early in the century. Excluding a short section in the Melynllyn Hone quarry, and possibly also at Hafod Las, it is unlikely that any such rails had been installed since Chwarel Ddu and Manod had laid them just before Waterloo.

Originally the Deeside tramway only served the Deeside quarry, running by gravity via their Nant y Pandy mill, to the head of an incline which oddly, was only later to run right into the railway yard. An extension, in conventional track, with an incline at each end, was made to Moelfferna in 1876 when the two quarries amalgamated, (necessitating the use of a gantry at Moelfferna to transfer from quarry gauge to tramway gauge). The whole was gravity worked, horses pulling back the empty waggons in the original FR. manner (although they walked, not rode, downwards). Penarth had an incline to the railway, but the smaller Cletwr carted to it.

The 1869 standard gauge Llanberis branch dramatically transformed the fortunes of the numerous quarries to the south of the village, most loading onto it via the Ffridd incline. This reduced their carriage to Caernarfon quay from at least 5/- (25p) per ton to well under 2/- (10p). For the first time, they could enter into serious competition with the mighty Dinorwig on the other side of Llyn Padarn.

Unfortunately the railways did not benefit all inland slate undertakings. The 1868 L. & N.W.R. Betws-y-coed branch ran on the eastern bank of the river, where there were no worthwhile quarries, thus further marginalising Dyffryn Conwy slate. In the Llangynog area, quarries such as Craig Rhiwarth, still had to cart to Llanymynech, just as long a trip as for the canal. (When the Tanat Valley line eventually opened in 1904, it was at least 30 years too late.) In short, if your quarry was on the railway, great, if it was not, tough. From around 1870 no quarry Sale Particulars were complete without an allusion to its 'proximity' to a railway, or if this could not be done, then at least a vague mention of a 'proposed' railway was included.

There was a further downside. There were many tiny isolated

workings at places such as the Elan valley in mid Wales, where small quarries had for centuries provided a slate of sorts for local requirements. With the best north Wales slate freely available at the nearest railway station, their crude product was no longer saleable.

Although the railways opened up several new quarrying areas, most of the output still came from Penrhyn, Dinorwig and Blaenau. Thus of far greater significance was their connection to the railway system. In 1852 a branch from the L. & N.W.R. Bangor-Caernarfon line was put into Port Penrhyn. Product from the quarry still came down the Penrhyn tramway, but from then on, it could be trans-shipped not just onto boats but also into railway waggons. A corresponding branch to Port Dinorwig, performed the same function. In 1872 the FR./Cambrian interchange at Minfford gave the Blaenau quarries a like facility, heralding the end of Porthmadog's expansion. These three connections alone, put over three-quarters of the total Welsh output of slate in touch with the national rail network. In addition, product from Nantlle had had since 1852, the opportunity to transfer to rail at Caernarfon docks. By 1864, the truncated Corris Railway no longer ran to the little shipping point at Derwenlas, but terminated at Machynlleth station. Although oddly, when the Cambrian and Wynne quarries in Glyn Ceiriog, after years of grappling with increasing tonnages by cart, at last in 1873 had a horse tramway, it ignored the Cambrian railway, which it actually crossed to reach the canal. It was only in 1888, when the line was steamed, that it was diverted to Chirk station.

Not all these rail-borne tonnages represented a loss to the ports. Tiles still cost more to make than slates. Only slate transport costs had enabled local tiles to remain competitive at inland locations. By the early 1870s there was scarcely any part of the U.K. where rail borne Welsh slate could not undercut the price of tiles. Thus much of what the railways carried was new business.

In 1874 the Cambrian Railways loaded well over 20,000 tons at Minffordd, but Porthmadog shipments from the quarries' wharves were four times that figure. Porthmadog shipments ceased to grow after 1878, but held up well for another 20 years and it would not be until 1905 that rail captured the majority of Blaenau tonnages.

At Port Penrhyn and Port Dinorwig their early rail connection and their quarries being by now less buoyant than those using Porthmadog, meant that their seaborne trade dwindled earlier, being overtaken by rail in the 1880s. But substantial shipments continued up to WW1, and some slate trade was retained at Port Dinorwig until the 1960s. At Caernarfon it was to be 1900 before the rail tonnage exceeded that of the port, and even then, in several subsequent years, less went by rail than by sea.

The comparative slowness of rail to capture trade was due to its expense. It was only an option for inland destinations. Coastwise shipment remained competitive for any traffic destined near to a seaport. For instance in 1880 the per ton rail carriage to London was 17/- (85p) against a sea-freight of at most 10/- (50p). Thus in spite of the speed and a reduced risk of breakage, the railways did not immediately replace the coastal vessels. This also applied to general cargos into north Wales which did not entirely disappear until the 1960s, displaced not by trains but by lorries.

However the effect of the railway on the port of Conwy was terminal, Rhos and Cwm Penmachno (the latter rapidly building up its workforce to 200) carted to the Betws-y-coed railhead and Tyn y Bryn had a direct rail connection by 1800. With no rail facilities at Conwy, what was shipped went out from the new rail-connected dock at Deganwy.

However it was not the steam locomotive but the steam ship which had the most dramatic effect on activity at the slate ports. Its arrival presaged the end of shipbuilding, already threatened by competition from low-cost Canadian yards. Steam engines were at first installed in wooden ships such as the 50 hp De Winton unit in Aberllefenni's Aberdyfi built 'Quarry Maid' of the 1850s, but progress soon demanded hulls of iron. The adzes of Wales had to yield to the riveting-hammers of England.

Although Porthmadog did lay down a few vessels in the 1890s and some building continued until 1913, by 1880 shipbuilding had all but ceased in north Wales. Iron and Steam also increased the size of ocean-going ships and although the likes of Penrhyn and Dinorwig operated fleets of iron steamers from their own ports, more and more deep-sea cargoes sailed from major ports such as Liverpool, increasingly reaching the dockside by rail. Thus even ahead of the decline and depression in the quarries the great partnership of shipping with slate, commenced its ebb into oblivion.

Fatal though the steam engine in its various forms was to prove to shipping, it was to be vital to the quarries in meeting the demands which burgeoned in the second half of the 19thC. Notably the Ffestiniog Railway, whose steaming in 1863 (in spite of vociferous objections by W.G. Oakeley's widow), enabled it to easily handle the near 70,000 tonnages which were overwhelming the horse/gravity working. The FR. was not the first steam hauled slate line, coming twenty years after Dinorwig's Padarn railway, but unlike the Padarn, it was to quarry gauge. It was the first successful steam railway in the world to operate on such a narrow gauge and one of the first to operate on appreciable gradients. Besides its influence on slate transport, the FR. became the model for many similar lines world-wide. Even today their engineers are consulted, their practices are copied and their technical leadership is acknowledged. Five years after the FR. was steamed, came the little Ffestiniog & Blaenau railway which acting as feeder to the FR., enabled Graig Ddu to have rail access, via its spectacular cascade of inclines, and offered handy rail transport to the small workings at Llan Ffestiniog.

This was followed in 1866 by the Talyllyn line which marked a stage in distribution development, as for the first time a quarry railway was laid down other than to a port. Running to the Cambrian line at Tywyn, slate could theoretically be carried to Aberdyfi. At first, like Corris traffic from Machynlleth that happened, and the line was hailed as a great benefit to the port, but the double handling involved gradually encouraged consignments to stay on rail. The Talyllyn was also unusual as although sponsored by Bryneglwys to carry its product, it was also a public railway. Its village incline and network of branches reached almost every dwelling in Abergynolwyn, so offering a 'door to door' service, surely the only railway ever to do so.

In 1868 the L. & N.W.R. built their Caernarfon to Afon Wen branch, superseding the Nantlle tramroad, whose roadbed it approximately followed to Penygroes. Four years later a sub-branch to Talysarn further truncated the Nantlle line. This cut the Nantlle quarries' carriage cost to Caernarfon quays from about 3/ (15p) to 2/3 (11p) per ton, but of course once on rail, there was every likelihood of it staying on rail, by-passing the port altogether.

The North Wales Narrow Gauge Railway of 1877 was part of a grand concept, of having a network of narrow gauge railways throughout north-west Wales. In a sense, it ran from nowhere to nowhere. For having failed to get access to Caernarfon, it started from Dinas, on the L. & N.W.R. Afon Wen branch, from where it was intended that slate would be carried to the port. Apart from the cost of double handling, again once slate was in a railway waggon it tended to stay there, further contributing to Caernarfon's decline. Its terminus was at bare wind-swept Rhyd Ddu, where apart from Snowdon climbers the only traffic was a few tons from Llyn y Gadair, Bwlch Cwm Llan and possibly Ffridd. A number of quarries in the Gwyrfai valley were served, but apart from Glanrafon, which it helped grow to a 250 man operation, and the much smaller Hafod y Wern, few were of any consequence. Its main slate traffic came via its Bryngwyn branch, which was almost entirely one long incline coming down from the head of the Nantlle valley, where it gave direct access to several quarries which hitherto had been dependent on cartage. The largest was Alexandra, which was reached by a most spectacular mile and a half looping rail line, down which for a time they sent over 4000 tons per year, others such as Braich and Moel Tryfan were able to get into the 2000 ton class, thanks to the N.W.N.G.R. This little railway's lack of commercial success was due to unfortunate timing as much as anything else, since its opening almost exactly coincided with a severe recession in the slate trade. After an almost terminal decline into the first years of the 20thC. It was revived by connection to Cilgwyn in 1923, but the tonnage which that quarry was by then turning out was a poor fraction of the 7-8000 tons they had once produced. There was a further revival in 1934 when it was extended to Porthmadog as the Welsh Highland Railway, using part of the Croesor tramway, but by that time there was virtually no slate traffic to be carried.

In 1879, the overworked and long outmoded Penrhyn tramway was replaced by the steam-powered Penrhyn Railway. Its terminations were the same as the horse-gravity tramway, but by following a more circuitous route there was no need for inclines. The same year the Corris railway also, was converted to steam.

On the other side of the coin, not all railways achieved their hoped-for tonnages. The expensive 1879 L & N.W.R. Blaenau extension up the Lledr valley attracted little traffic, of the Blaenau quarries, only Llechwedd was able to conveniently reach it. Though they could either load onto railway waggons or have their quarry waggons carried pic-a-back to the Deganwy slate quays via a direct interchange, they used the facility mainly as a weapon to obtain reduced rates from the FR., other quarries made some use of the L. & N.W.R. particularly W.S.C. successor Oakeley, but they did not have a direct link to it until 1934. The 1882 G.W.R. Blaenau branch from Bala, offered spectacular views for passengers, but never succeeded in capturing much slate traffic. Apart from a trifle picked up from the quarries around Llan Ffestiniog, it mainly served as a feeder for the FR. carrying Graig Ddu quarry trucks, again pic-a-back, the couple of miles to Blaenau. Thus virtually only continuing the function of the Ffestiniog and Blaenau railway, whose alignment it approximately followed. Similarly the L. & N.W.R. Bethesda branch of 1884, brought some benefit to a handful of small independent quarries, (none of which were directly connected), but it cannot have ever repaid its construction costs.

In south Wales, surprisingly, in view of the small outputs, two standard gauge lines were built partly to carry slate traffic. Although of the quarries the 1873 Cardigan Railway was intended to serve, Pencelli and Penlan were unsuccesful, Glogue did better, employing up to over 80 men and surviving until 1926. A curious feature of the line was that though the relatively active Fforest quarries, were closely skirted, they never used the railway, continuing to boat down the Tyfi to Cardigan up to their 1885 closure. The Maenclochog Railway of 1876, was initially planned to open up the Rosebush quarry, which thus given access to the G.W.R. enjoyed some short-lived prosperity. In addition to these there was also the 2 mile Abereiddi tramroad built in the 1850s to link that quarry with Porthgain harbour.

Apart from their primary function, all these lines brought general benefit to local communities, many of which without the lure of slate traffic would not have had the advantage of rail transport. Indeed some of the little tramways such as the Hendre Ddu, Ratgoed and Croesor opened up totally roadless valleys. Railways also changed employment patterns. Labour catchment was no longer limited by the distance a man could walk, and in some cases gave a quarryman for the first time, a choice of employer, thus if he was laid off, it eased the problem of obtaining alternative work (provided he was not blacklisted!). On the other hand, it meant, as would become manifest towards the end of the century, that during a strike an employer could more readily bring in outside labour. The railways altered barracking and lodging practices, many more men could now live at home and barrackers and lodgers could now come from much further afield, such as the occupants of the Anglesey barracks at Dinorwig. Coming mainly from the Llanidan area, they had to leave home at 3.00 am on a Monday morning to walk to the ferry.

The main line railways offered cheap workmen's tickets, the FR. and Talyllyn provided workmen's trains. Quarrymen were carried on the Penrhyn steam railway almost from its start. Later the Padarn had workmen's trains, for many years they had permitted the men to use their own man-powered vehicles. These 'Velocipedes' usually had 4 seats, each equipped with pedals[2]. The little Hendre Ddu tramroad at one time carried quarrymen free.

The steam locomotive also had a great impact on internal quarry transport. Obviously the very small quarries were not users of locomotives, but the bigger ones with literally miles of track (up to

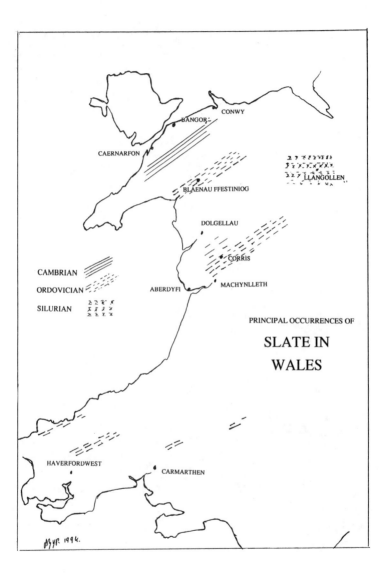

BANGOR
CONWY
CAERNARFON
LLANGOLLEN
BLAENAU FFESTINIOG
DOLGELLAU
CORRIS
CAMBRIAN
ORDOVICIAN
ABERDYFI
MACHYNLLETH
SILURIAN

PRINCIPAL OCCURRENCES OF

SLATE IN
WALES

HAVERFORDWEST
CARMARTHEN

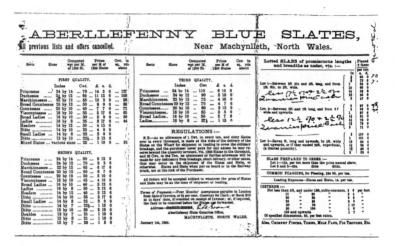

Price Card of 1890, Aberllefenni Quarry

Train of empty slate waggons on Rhiwbach Tramroad c 1900
By kind permission of Mr G.R. Jones

Working in a chamber, Bwlch y Slaters c 1960
By kind permission of Mr Dafydd Price

Gelli Grin wharf on the Dwyryd. Etching by Alfred Clint
from Bennetts Guide Through North Wales. (Colburn 1838)
By kind permission of the executors of the late Mr W.J. Hitchings

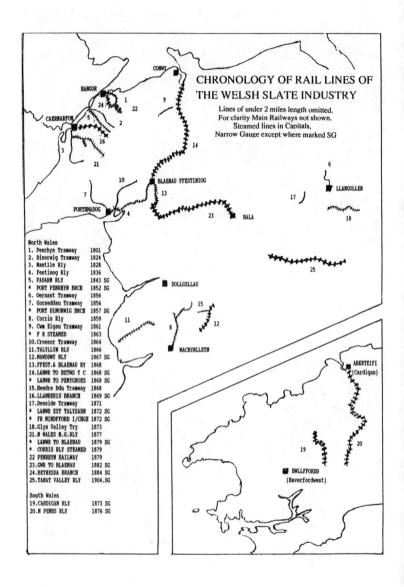

CHRONOLOGY OF RAIL LINES OF
THE WELSH SLATE INDUSTRY

Lines of under 2 miles length omitted.
For clarity Main Railways not shown.
Steamed lines in Capitals,
Narrow Gauge except where marked SG

North Wales
1. Penrhyn Tramway   1801
2. Dinorwig Tramway   1824
3. Nantile Rly   1828
4. Festinog Rly   1836
5. PADARN RLY   1843 SG
* PORT PENRHYN BRCH   1852 SG
6. Oernant Tramway   1856
7. Gorseddau Tramway   1856
* PORT DINORWIG BRCH   1857 SG
8. Corris Rly   1859
9. Cwm Eigau Tramway   1861
* F R STEAMED   1863
10. Croesor Tramway   1864
11. TALYLLYN RLY   1866
12. MAWDDWY RLY   1867 SG
13. FFEST.& BLAENAU RY   1868
14. L&NWR TO BETWS Y C   1868 SG
* L&NWR TO PENYGROES   1868 SG
15. Hendre Ddu Tramway   1868
16. LLANBERIS BRANCH   1869 SG
17. Deeside Tramway   1871
* L&NWR EXT TALYSARN   1872 SG
* FR MINDFFORD I/CHGE   1872 SG
18. Glyn Valley Try   1873
21. N WALES N.G.RLY   1877
* L&NWR TO BLAENAU   1879 SG
* CORRIS RLY STEAMED   1879
22 PENRHYN RAILWAY   1879
23. GWR TO BLAENAU   1882 SG
24. BETHESDA BRANCH   1884 SG
25. TANAT VALLEY RLY   1904. SG

South Wales
19. CARDIGAN RLY   1873 SG
20. N PEMBS RLY   1876 SG

Handling rubbish, Bwlch y Slaters c 1960
By kind permission of Mr Dafydd Price

Handling block, Bwlch y Slaters c 1960
By kind permission of Mr Dafydd Price

Mill interior, Blaenau Ffestiniog 1890s?
By permission Gwynedd Archives Service

Writing slate factory, probably at Bangor late 19thC

Handling block, Bwlch y Slaters c 1960
By kind permission of Mr Dafydd Price

Locomotive, Penrhyn 1964
Author's collection

Australia Mill, Dinorwig c 1985
Author's collection

Wiresawing at Llechwedd 1994
By kind permission of J.W. Greaves & Sons Ltd

Penrhyn 1964
Author's collection

Gwaliau, Foel c 1985
Author's collection

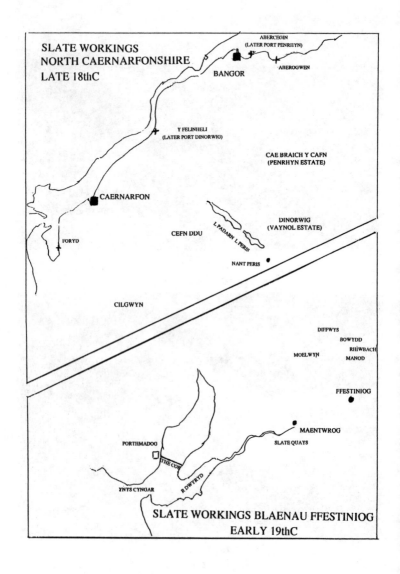

SLATE WORKINGS
NORTH CAERNARFONSHIRE
LATE 18thC

ABERCEGIN
(LATER PORT PENRHYN)

BANGOR

ABEROGWEN

Y FELINHELI
(LATER PORT DINORWIG)

CAE BRAICH Y CAFN
(PENRHYN ESTATE)

CAERNARFON

CEFN DDU

L PADARN L PERIS

DINORWIG
(VAYNOL ESTATE)

NANT PERIS

FORYD

CILGWYN

DIFFWYS

BOWYDD

MOELWYN

RHIWBACH

MANOD

FFESTINIOG

MAENTWROG

PORTHMADOG

THE COB

SLATE QUAYS

YNYS CYNGAR

R DWYRYD

SLATE WORKINGS BLAENAU FFESTINIOG
EARLY 19thC

Drumhouse gear, Hollands quarry dating from 1830s? c 1980
Author's collection

Slab and Jwmpah Llechwedd
By kind permission of J.W. Greaves & Sons Ltd

Brine bath resistors, Maenofferen c 1975
Author's collection

Ladders Pen yr Orsedd c 1990
Author's collection

Slab waggons at No 5 Mill, Llechwedd c 1970
Author's collection

Rubbish Waggon on Blondin, Pen yr Orsedd c 1975
Author's collection

Incline and steps Gloddfa Ganol 1994
Author's collection

Slate Splitting at Llechwedd 1994
By kind permission of J.W. Greaves & Sons Ltd

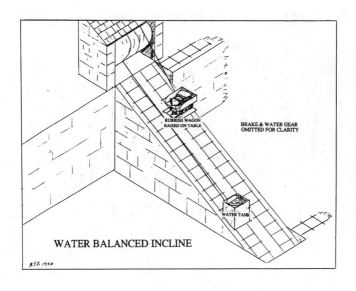

RUBBISH WAGON
RAISED ON TABLE

BRAKE & WATER GEAR
OMITTED FOR CLARITY

WATER TANK

WATER BALANCED INCLINE

A.T.R 1944

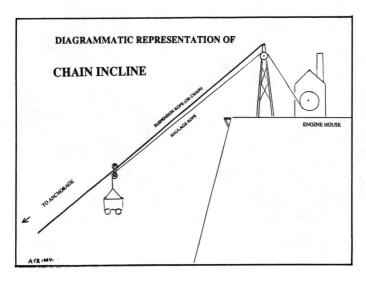

DIAGRAMMATIC REPRESENTATION OF

CHAIN INCLINE

SUSPENSION ROPE (OR CHAIN)

HAULAGE ROPE

ENGINE HOUSE

TO ANCHORAGE

A.T.R 1944

Mr Dafydd Price splitting slate, Bwlch y Slaters c 1960
By kind permission of Mr Dafydd Price

50 miles in the case of Dinorwig) certainly were. Though some quarries such as Dorothea found employment for a horse or two until well after WW2, from the late 1860s the larger, and some not so large quarries, started to introduce locos for their longer hauls. The first quarry to have a loco was probably Glynrhonwy Lower in about 1866. It was certainly a De Winton, these vertical boilered units soon becoming the standard prime-mover in many slate and other quarries. Although supplanted by more efficient designs, some remained in use for almost a century.

Dorothea had locos by 1869, which called for the laying of 2' track for them to run on, as their existing rails were to the 3'6" Nantlle gauge. Dinorwig had locos by 1870, shortly followed by the Welsh Slate Company, and in 1874 by both Llechwedd and the newly amalgamated Votty & Bowydd. Penrhyn had them by 1876, eventually building up to a fleet of more than 30. Like Dinorwig they eventually had a loco on almost every one of their many galleries, as well as using them in the mill areas and at their ports. Glynrhonwy Upper put in their first by 1877, which ran both in tunnels and on a frighteningly flimsy platform cantilevered out from a rock face. The same year Pen yr Orsedd began to build up their fleet to an astonishing 12.

With the coming of the N.W.N.G.R. several of the larger quarries it served put in locos. Alexandra, Glanrafon and Moel Tryfan each had 3. At about the same time, Cilgwyn, Pen y Bryn and Talysarn, also went in for them and by 1880 even little Coed Madog had 3 De Wintons. Eventually quite small quarries, such as Fron, Pant Dreiniog, Rhos, Abercwmeiddaw and Manod used steam traction. One of the most interesting uses was in Cambrian quarry at Glyn Ceiriog where steam locos hauled through their almost 900 yards long tunnel.

Little steam locos, grumbling and teetering along undulating tracks became almost as characteristic of slate quarrying as the drumhouse and incline. They were still being acquired, second-hand, well into the 1930s. Some remained in use until the 1960s, long after they had become uncompetitive with petrol or diesel units. Such I.C. locos started to appear in small numbers at the beginning of the 20thC. supplanting steam in a big way during the inter-war years. A few were new, most were second-hand, including ex WW1 army units, but a number were built in the quarries own workshops.

Outside the quarries, apart from limited use of diesel by the FR., in the inter-war years, and the primitive 'lash ups' of the Hendre Ddu tramway, the slate railways, as opposed to the internal quarry lines, remained faithful to steam. Though most of these are long gone, thanks to enthusiasts, such as those of the FR. the Talyllyn and other groups, the sound of puffing and whistling, still echoes in the Gwynedd mountains.

---

[1] These Insurance Societies, did not charge premiums but made calls on their members if and when a loss took place. They survived up to WW1, when the rate of sinkings finally overwhelmed them. In their later years they undoubtedly helped wooden sailing vessels to be kept in service as towards the end of the 19thC. the general Marine Insurance market charged prohibitive premiums on them.

[2] The only other known instance of a line being officially used for 'commuting' with private 'vehicles' was at Craig Ddu. There men descended the inclines on 'ceir gwyllt' (wild cars). These resembled a modern skateboard, which ran on one rail of one track, with an outrigger to a wheel running on one rail of the other track. Persons familiar with the steepness of the Craig Ddu Inclines may have some difficulty in believing this!

7. The Golden Years
1860-1877

By 1860 Welsh slate could look back on thirty years of expansion. During the 1830s almost every year had brought increased demand. There were both booms and setbacks in the 1840s, but trade picked up again in the early 1850s in the wake of the Great Exhibition and the abolition of the tax on brick. The Crimean war dampened demand, but its end brought a new peak in 1857, followed by a slight weakening in 1858.

Over those thirty years, output had shown considerable growth but it had been an unsteady climb along a giddy switchback of peaks and troughs. Prices had varied in a similar way, rising sharply when demand increased, levelling off as supply caught up and falling when demand faltered. But, whereas the trend of output was inexorably upward, that of prices was not. No matter how brisk the times, prices never rose more than about 10-15% above the bumper era of 1814/15 and always within 4 or 5 years had plummeted again.

Then, in 1860 the switchback stopped. Not only did prices rise to a new record, but all through the '60s, it was up all the way, each year's price lists setting further records, until by 1869, they were 25% up on those of a decade before. Neither were there any setbacks in output, total Welsh production reaching 350,000 tons before the 60's were out. Over 100,00 tons came from Bethesda, mostly from Penrhyn but with an appreciable contribution from the over 300 men now at Pandreiniog, Tan y Bwlch, Bryn Hafod y Wern and Moelfaban. Blaenau's tonnage almost equalled Bethesda's, largely due to the Welsh Slate Company's output almost doubling in less than five years. Both Holland's, and Mathew's had five figure tonnages, with Cwmorthin and Llechwedd not far behind. The amalgamated Votty & Bowydd and Diffwys were not much smaller, and half a dozen others had four figure outputs. It is a measure of the optimism of the times that though Diffwys had failed to match the expansion of its neighbours, it still fetched £120,000, when sold in 1863 (it had been bought in 1801 for £1,000). At Llanberis the 80,000 tons produced by Dinorwig's 2400 or so men dominated the area, but with the Glynrhonwys, and their half dozen neighbours' now employing over 250 men, their contribution was not negligible, and would shortly expand further with rail connection. Nantlle's near 2000 men accounted for 40,000 tons, about a quarter from Dorothea's 500 men, and with Pen yr Orsedd temporarily faltering, Cilgwyn, Pen y Bryn and Tal y Sarn's, 800 men produced much of the remainder. The rest of the Welsh industry amounted to about 20,000 tons.

Right through the 60's, the trade press complained of extended delivery times, up to 47 weeks being cited. Quarries, besides deriving the obvious benefits, were able to pick and choose to whom they sold, thus bad debt, always the bane of the industry, fell. Large minimum order quantities were demanded and Penrhyn and Dinorwig exacted surcharges on orders of less than 30 tons. Quarries competed for manpower pushing wages up in some cases to exceed 5/- (25p) per day[1]. There was a spate of re-openings of previously unsuccessful quarries, such as Alltgoch at Aberdyfi, invariably accompanied by press accounts of ambitious plans. Spurred by the 1862 Companies Act, there was unprecedented speculative investment, and in the four years which followed it, 58 companies were formed to run slate quarries in north Wales. Most never actually operated, some were attempts to off-load fundamentally unprofitable quarries, but some such as those at Hafod Las and Rhiwgoch were genuine and successful attempts to put a working on a sounder financial footing by attracting new capital to cope with expansion.

All this prosperity was too good to last and in 1870 the Franco-Prussian war halted the climb. Back to the old boom and bust? Far from it, in 1872, the market recovered and prices resumed their seemingly unstoppable rise. By 1875 Blaenau prices for Princesses were £13.50 per mille, against the £8.25 of 1850. Ladies were £5.50 against £2.75 and unlike earlier boom times, the smaller sizes showed even greater gains, Doubles fetching £2.25, up from £0.75. In the same period wages had risen perhaps 50%

and other costs not at all, there was now real money to be made. Penrhyn was said to be netting over £100,000 per year, and Welsh Slate were reported as making well over £1 per ton clear profit on their 60,000 ton output, even after paying a royalty of 4/6 (22.5p) per ton to the Oakeleys, (who were thus collecting almost £14,000 p.a. from this quarry alone). This was not a boom, it was a bonanza.

Demand exploded, some quarries' attitude to customers bordered on the cavalier. Increasingly onerous minimum order quantities and all sorts of surcharges were imposed. Some insisted that orders be executed in sizes and grades to their, not the buyer's choice. There even developed something of a 'Black Market', with desperate users paying over the odds to get supplies. Unfortunately buyers' anxiety to secure slate was not always matched by an alacrity in paying for it. This was nothing new, but increased tonnages at higher prices meant larger debts being carried, straining many a quarry's finances. In fact in 1877 at the height of the boom, Maenofferen was being threatened by its creditors, and the Cwmorthin company was in difficulties.

With huge price increases even for the poorest product, the humblest of diggings had profit potential. The trade press was reporting 'new Openings' almost every month, most of which came to nothing, as virtually every worth-while site was already taken. Every likely looking bit of rock was dug or tunnelled, in increasingly improbable locations, usually backed by highly suspect promotions. The trade press habitually carried warnings against unwise speculation, which were just as habitually ignored. Little more than a rumour of slate, was enough to get a company floated.

Searches were made further and further away from proven areas, sometimes with luck, more often without. Men beavered away in such places as Cwm Bronchiau, in south Meirionnydd. Having brought to the surface perhaps a thousand tons of almost useless rock, they repeated the same futile exercise at Gyllellog. At Fronheulog and other places in the Tywyn hinterland, there was frantic digging to find rock. In south Wales at Ystrad Ffin, 1½ miles of highly engineered road was built to reach an insignificant outcrop.

If absolutely useless rock was encountered, it was confidently stated that *'Excellent material will be found when a greater depth is reached'*. It rarely was, although there was some truth in this as rock near the surface could well be degraded by weathering. Enthusiasm was expressed for improbable developments as being *'On a new north facing opening'*. Again with some truth, as slate taken from a working face in direct sunlight could prove too dry to give a good split.

It is a measure of the optimism of the times, that in 1873 only a few miles from where the Gorseddau mill remained as a most prominent reminder of the follies of a generation before, Prince of Wales quarry was expensively developed. A layout similar to and only slightly less ambitious than Gorseddau was constructed. To obviate the extravagant 12/6 (62.5p) cost of carrying to Caernarfon via the head of Cwm Pennant, the Gorseddau tramway was extended and re-gauged to 2', and a De Winton loco bought. With 200 men at work it briefly reached a respectable 5000 tons, but in spite of venturing underground and making a further opening at the nearby but almost inaccessible Princess, good rock eluded them. With mounting losses on a falling market, it closed in 1886.

Some did not even get that far. In 1875, at Cambergi, near Corris, a group of south Wales industrialists, laid out terraces, built an incline, mill etc., leaving them with no money to work the quarry which they abandoned within 2 years, having scarcely made any product at all.

At Escairgeiliog, near Machynlleth, the Cambria Wynne Slate Quarry Company beggared themselves, opening Cwm Gloddfa and building a grand mill. Local men took it on, but they too failed, with the proverbial third owner eventually making something of a go of it.

In the Porthmadog hinterland there had been, in the mid 1860s, a couple of moderate (30 men) developments, Berthllwyd, and Gerynt, but neither survived more than 10 years, and the modest

Dolfriog had an even shorter life. By the mid 70s there was renewed interest in the area with openings at Hafoty and Hafod Uchaf, both employed about 12 men, and had water-powered mills (although machinery was never installed at Hafod Uchaf), neither lasted long. Shortly afterwards Cwm Caeth was opened also with a small mill. In the classic manner, when output and returns tailed off in 1886, the Aberglaslyn Slate Quarry & Enamelled Co was formed to take it over but within 6 years it had again failed. Nearer Porthmadog, there was a revival at Porthreuddyn, where a very tough slab was brought out, which made excellent doorsteps. But the other dozen and a half attempts in that area to revive old small workings, or make new ones met with scant success.

Some developments bordered on the bizarre, at Cyfanned where lead had been worked from around the 1840s, the crushing of ore was abandoned, and attention turned to the slate vein which their workings had fortuitously encountered. Something similar may also have occurred at Hafod Boeth. At Brithdir, near Llanfyllin, a little phosphate working was deemed to have slate potential, so in 1880 a company was formed and machinery bought second-hand from Bryneglwys, with the vain intention of making framed writing slates. Conversely metals were allegedly found in the course of slate working, as happened at Dolgarth, Braich Goch and elsewhere, such reports may have been exaggerations to encourage investors, but it is possible that the moderately successful copper mine at Cwm Dwyfor arose out of unsuccessful slate trials. The metal working at nearby Moelfre, predated and had no connection with the slate quarry.

Not all developments were unsuccessful, unscrupulous or crazy. In 1874, fairly good rock was found at the head of Cwm Orthin and opened up as Conglog, it had a mill and an extension of the Cwmorthin tramway provided good transport. Though modest and only worked part time by two brothers for much of its 30 year life, they presumably made money, as it is alleged that the postmaster at Tanygrisiau, who acted as their banker, absconded with their accumulated takings! Such working of tiny quarries part-time was an ongoing feature of the industry, often by just one or two men who also held down full time jobs in a larger quarry.

There were several new workings in the Llangollen area such as Craig y Glem and Craig Wynnstay, which were in a modest way viable. A little to the south, at Cwmmaengwynedd 3 or 4 men beavered underground, and at nearby Llangynog there were new diggings.

In south Wales too, there was activity, some workings such as Rosebush and Llangolman being reasonably successful, but less luck was had at the many more marginal sites.

In 1873 the Mining Journal carried extracts from a series of articles in the *Caernarvon and Denbigh Herald*. They give a valuable insight into the state of quarrying at the time as seen by a layman[2].

Of Dolwyddelan the correspondent reported that '*Prince Llywelyn and Penllyn are being worked by companies, a few men are at Rhiw Goch but Fedw is idle*'.

In the south of Meirionnydd he said that '*Bryneglwys has 260 men working on 5 Levels and in the hills, barracks, houses and a Writing Slate factory. At Gaewern, the Talyllyn Slate Company have some chambers open, there is a spacious machine room, all rubbish is sent down an incline the loaded waggon rolling downwards enabling a weighted ballast waggon to return* (i.e. a single acting incline) *Braich Goch has 200 men and 2 machine rooms, one being at Gaewern. The new Cambria Wynne has 50 men on slab work only. Aberllefenni has workings on 3 sites and there are a further 3 quarries, Cymerau, Ratgoed and Hendre Ddu to the north. Mr Buckley has workings at Dinas Mawddwy*'.

Of Nantlle, he said, '*7 Veins are worked, the principal quarries being Alexandra, Moel Tryfan, Braich, Fron, Pen yr Orsedd, Cilgwyn, Gallt Fedw, Pan y Bryn, Dorothea, Talysarn, Cloddfa'r Coed, Coed Madog, Gwernor, Tŷ Mawr* (Tŷ Mawr West?), *Nantlle* (Nantlle Vale?), *Tŷ'n y Weirglodd, Nant yr Allt* (Tan yr Allt?) *and Fronheulog. Of these Dorothea is the largest with 450-500 men, owned by John Williams & Company. Cilgwyn employs 260 men and has abandoned 2 of its 4 pits, whilst Pen y Bryn employs 300 men in 4 pits.*

John Robinson is said to be the owner of several quarries through the Talysarn Slate Quarry Company including Gallt y Fedw, where only 12 men are working, and Gloddfa'r Coed which is flooded. Braich is a large pit on 3 floors, with 140 men and where the Dixon Manual Drill is used, with one man turning the drill, whilst another pumps water into the hole'.

A particularly picturesque description was given of Dorothea — *'Rockmen are working upon different ledges of rock, some with levers forcing open splits in the rock, others regularly plying the long chisel. Rubblemen were noisily throwing waste rubble into small iron waggons, which as soon as loaded, ascend the inclined chains'.*

Of Dinorwig, he said, *'Mr G.W.D. Assheton-Smith's quarry includes the old Garret section and the new, comprising Wellington, near the old quarry, Victoria further south, Braich above Victoria and Matilda and Sophia above Wellington. There are inclines to Garret, Wellington and Victoria. Allt Ddu one of the oldest is worked as a pit. The hours are 6am to 5.30 with meals from 10-11 and 3-3.30, taken in cabins of 30 or 40 men. New houses are replacing barracks'.*

Of Cwm Pennant he said, *'There is Prince Llywelyn, previously known as Hendre Ddu and the recently re-opened Moelfre has 20-30 men and a fine water-wheel for sawing and planing. Prince of Wales now on 7 galleries is still carrying slate over to Rhyd Ddu, but has purchased an old tramway'.*

At Bethesda, *'Penrhyn has 2800 men at work, there is a hospital among trees and there are 6 waterbalances in use. Pantdreiniog is being worked by the Bangor and Pantdreiniog Slate Company and Tan y Bwlch by the Port Bangor Slate Company. Bryn Hafod y Wern, run by the Royal Bangor Slate company has a pit 74 yards deep'.*

In the Blaenau area, after mentioning the 278 men at Diffwys and the 310 at Votty & Bowydd, at the Welsh Slate Company's quarry he became almost poetic *'Imagine such a chamber — the daylight streaming through the upper opening, the bottom only to be recognised by the small lights of the workmen, and yourself perched midway between dawn and midnight on a small wooden bridge, while the horrible rumbling of the explosion comes rolling through the passages till the bridge beneath your feet vibrates in conscious fear.'* At Drum he rather fell into condescension '*I reached the quarry at noon, and was allowed the privilege of steaming my clothes before a peat fire in the weight-taker's hut. The men soon came filing in, each man taking a can from the fireplace. That can contained neither tea nor coffee but butter milk. I entered into off hand conversation with the men and soon found that in politics they were eminently radical in sympathies, generally warm hearted and as impulsive as Celts in general'.*

All the time, expansion was continuing, much of it attributable to exports. From 1861 to 1881 Nantlle output, very much export driven, increased from 30,000 to 74,000 tons, but Blaenau went from under 70,000 to approaching 150,000 tons[3].

Since the beginning of the century the output of Bethesda and Nantlle had expanded fourfold, that of Llanberis sevenfold, whereas Blaenau expansion was more than a hundredfold. This was reflected in the population growth of Ffestiniog parish from 732 in 1801 to 11,274 in 1881. Penrhyn and Dinorwig continued to be by far the largest units, but their 1882 outputs of 111,000 and 87,000 tons respectively, would prove to be their zeniths. Their dominance was waning and the centre of gravity was moving towards Blaenau.

Inland quarries, thanks to the railways were doing well, the Corwen area raised over 4000 tons in 1882, but the Oernant quarries without direct access to a railway produced only 3000 tons, little more than half of their total 30 years earlier. The quarries on Cefn Ddu benefiting from the 1869 Llanberis branch, were boosted further by the 1878 extension of the Ffridd incline and the amalgamation of Cambrian, Cefn Ddu and Goodman's. This pushed their output to some 5000 tons per year, but they were entering a mature market where buyers had become used to the famous names, this would make them vulnerable when a downturn enabled buyers to be more choosy. The same thing applied at Corris where the steaming of the Corris railway came too late for them to be a force in the market-place, at least as far as roofing-slate was concerned. In Dyffryn Conwy, even at the height of the boom scarcely 6000 tons was produced, a fraction of what their output once had been.

Not that Wales was the only source of slate. The rest of the U.K. (which then included Ireland), was by the late 1870s, producing over 50,000 tons, but this was still dwarfed by the Welsh total of 450,000 tons. The Welsh quarries were also more profitable, their sales averaging 53/- (£2.65) per ton, whereas the rest of the U.K. could barely manage 37/- (£1.85). Added to which, the 14259 men in the Welsh quarries each averaged over 31 tons per year, but in the rest of the U.K. the average was only some 28 tons. Imports did not yet pose an overwhelming threat but ominously their value in 1878 was £20,000, three times the total of barely twenty years before.

To some extent the good times were shared by the men. In about 30 years wages had increased considerably, in the 1840s, as little as 1/- (5p) per day, for an adult labourer was not unknown, with a top bargainer making 3/- (15p). By the mid 70s almost double these figures were commonplace with some Blaenau men making 7/- (35p). Besides which, in the same period, the cost of living had fallen. Flour at 3/- (15p) the half-peck, had not gone down, and in fact went up after the bad harvests of 1875-78. But the vital tea and sugar had more than halved to 3/- lb. (15p) and 3½d lb. (1.4p) respectively. Soap and starch, essential to the proud wives, had also dropped by similar amounts. Quarrymen were able to indulge their craving for books, paying off pedlars weekly for weighty tomes. In Blaenau, at least, it was not unknown for quarrymen to have a live-in servant. These girls, some as young as 10, may have been relatives, working for next to nothing to gain experience, but their presence indicates a degree of housekeeping surplus, amongst some workers.

Though quarrymen might now feel almost affluent, compared with their fathers, their rewards were in sharp contrast with the profits made by some of the large proprietors. Also in contrast too, with the revenues of some of the quarries' landlords, particularly if they were on an advalorem royalty. A small quarry, ill-sited on poor rock with uneconomic transport and onerous lease-terms, no matter how hungry the market or how high the prices, could rarely make money. But a quarry close to a rail line, able to usefully employ, say 100 plus men on good rock and with little or no royalty, could, in the mid 1870s, be very profitable indeed.

Undoubtedly some of the reports of enormous profits made at that time, do not fully reflect the amortisation of development and plant, or of the 'wasting asset' nature of any extractive undertaking. Unfortunately, many proprietors took an equally simplistic view. It is rare to find financial accounts which include adequate write-downs of equipment, and sums spent on development work was often accumulated in balance sheets as 'assets'. Unsaleable stock was, one suspects, frequently overvalued and funds were certainly not set aside for plant modernisation or renewal. It was quite usual for any monies in hand at the end of the year to be declared a 'profit'. Improper, but understandable where there were shareholders to be satisfied or lenders to be kept happy. Where there were neither, it was not just self-delusion, it was folly. When profits, real or illusory, were increasing year by year it did not much matter. When they ceased to grow, it did, as many were to find out.

Looking at figures in retrospect, there was another cause for concern. Whenever any commodity rises in price there is pressure to look for, or to develop, a substitute. Throughout the century, other than a brief period during the Napoleonic wars when the delivered price of Welsh slate was inflated both by the Slate Duty and war-risk shipping rates, it had been cheaper, often substantially cheaper, to roof with slate rather than tile in places close to ports. The coming of the railways had extended this advantage to very many inland destinations. However the big price increases of the 1860s & 70s eroded this difference, until by the mid 1870s, both materials were virtually on a par in important markets such as the south-east of England. Tile makers would need to only slightly improve their methods to underprice slate.

[1] Blaenau average daily wages (G.J. Williams)

	Quarryman	Miner	Labourer
1860	4/3 (21p)	3/3 (16p)	2/6 (12.5p)-3/- (15p)
1865	5/- (25p)	4/2 (21p)	3/- (15p) — 3/6 (17/5p)
1870	5/6 (27.5p)	4/6 (22.5p)	3/6 (17.5p) 3/9 (17.6p)

[2] These are reproduced in full in The Slate Quarries of North Wales edited by Dr. M.J.T. Lewis (see bibliography)

[3] Some Blaenau tonnages

	1840	1859	1879
Wrysgan	?	1235	2078
Diffwys	?	?	5567
Maenofferen	?	700	8366
Cwmorthin	?	?	10736
Votty & Bowydd	?	8964	12092
Holland's	10580	10676	13739
Mathew's	2390	9287	15161
Llechwedd	—	7900	18269
Welsh Slate	9337	26236	43296

8. Trouble and Strife
The 1880s

The good times did not last. In 1875 after almost 20 years of vigorous growth the British economy took a downturn. The building industry was badly hit, but with outstanding orders to fill and merchants' stocks to replenish, the full effects were not felt by the quarries until well into 1876. The 1877 lists were shaved to try to stimulate demand, this exercise being repeated in ensuing years until at the end of 1880 there were signs of recovery. Some quarries which had been on 4 day working went back to a full week, and several which had closed were talking of re-opening. At the end of the year a 6000 ton order from Hamburg brought Christmas cheer to Blaenau. Nevertheless, the owners, who were now for almost the first time getting together to agree prices, shaded them again for 1881. Their reading of the prospects was correct since demand again slackened.

With prices eased and supplies freely available, buyers could be more selective. Thus those quarries able to make larger sizes and higher qualities, particularly if they had a 'known name', were not dramatically affected by the downturn. However those locked into lower grades had to savagely slash their prices to move their product, seriously threatening their viability. Furthermore poor productivity, endemic in many smaller quarries, could no longer be offset by high prices.

Figures for Caernarfonshire in 1882 based on average 'at quarry' valuation, show how much profitability varied. They are not a precise comparison as they do not reflect royalties, equipment amortisation, nor coal and other costs, but they do give useful rough comparison.

The two Superquarries led this 'League Table'. Penrhyn obtained £2.43 per ton which at 39.6 tons per man year gave a gross return per employee of £96.28. Dinorwig on £2.20 and 38.7 tpmy obtained a return of £85.14 per man, which their large workforces multiplied into very large sums, uneroded by royalties.

Some Nantlle quarries obtained good prices. Dorothea material was averaging £3.10 and although the productivity of their 533 men, in their difficult pit-working conditions was only 31, it still gave them a revenue of £96.10 per man. A useful figure, making them, Dinorwig and Penrhyn apart, the county's most profitable unit, and the only Nantlle quarry to ever show consistent profits. By contrast, neighbouring South Dorothea although getting a handsome £3.60 per ton, their 70 men raised a mere 14 tons each dropping their per-man take to little more than £50.00 Pen yr Orsedd with their 1870s problems behind them, were back up to 261 men, making 7999 tons, equalling Dorothea's productivity, but since they could only get £2.60 per ton, this dropped their take to about £79.60 per man. Cilgwyn averaged the same price as Pen yr Orsedd, but since their 300 men only raised 24.6 tons each, this dropped their revenue to under £70.00.

Tal y Sarn's prices were on a par with Dorothea, but needing 400 men to raise 8210 tons they only grossed £63.60 per man. Alexandra got a useful £3.17 per ton and with the output of their 195 men on 23 tpmy, took almost £73.00 on each. Nearby Moel Tryfan could only get £2.19, which at 23 tons gave a return of barely £50.00 on each of their 81 men. Braich was able to average £2.40 per ton but with their 124 men only turning out 21 tons each, their figure was £54.60. Coed Madoc got the same price as Braich but getting less than 19 tons per man from their workforce of 100, the return was less than £45.00.

Over at Llanberis, Glynrhonwy was obtaining £2.20 and with their 53 men each turning out 28.6 tons, they grossed almost £63.00 per man, and at Cefn Du on the same price and with productivity only slightly less, each of their 197 men brought in just under £62.00. The best that Cook & Ddol could obtain was £2.07 and with their 26 men returning 23 tons their revenue on each was only £47.61.

At Bethesda, Bryn Hafod y Wern's 65 men raised a creditable 33.8 tons each, but which only realised a meagre £1.27 per ton, giving a return of about £43.00 per man. Any worries this quarry may have had about poor revenues became academic in 1889. The new Lord Penrhyn may have felt that they were taking business he considered rightfully his, and he may have been mindful of the rebuff received by his predecessor when he had tried to annex the site. For whatever reason, he cut off the quarry's water supply which was sourced on his land. Since this 'upside down' quarry had to haul all its rock, rubbish included, out of a pit, all power for which, and for mill driving, was from water, this brought immediate closure.

At Penmachno 100 men raised over 44 tons each which at £1.75 gave the quarry £77.00 per man. This low selling price and high productivity suggesting that as at Bryn Hafod y Wern, there was a high proportion of slab. Such high slab outputs were also reflected in the 50 tons per man achieved at Penarth and Moelfferna. At Hafod Las, nearly 700 tons (including building block) was being raised by only 10 men, which even selling at only £1.29 per ton, gave a revenue of £86.30 from each.

Other quarries were clearly running at a loss, even on a current expenditure basis. Glanrafon averaged over £3.00 for its product, but with its 97 men each raising scarcely 10 tons, it grossed only £31.00 per man. Even the much larger Pen y Bryn with its 234 men had a productivity figure of less than 12 tons, so even getting £2.50 per ton grossed them under £30.00 per man. New Fronheulog could only obtain £2.23 but with productivity of their 98 men at 16 tons, they were somewhat better off at £35.68. Fron was getting £2.20, but since the productivity of their 62 strong workforce was under 12 tons their revenue was only about £26.00 per man. At little Garreg Fawr 6 men could only manage 80 tons which at £2.00 per ton gave them a gross per man of under £27.00. Prince Llywelyn's 74 men raised only 25 tons each, which realised under £1.00 per ton, a disastrous revenue situation. This was an example of a quarry only able to turn out small and lower grade roofing slates, being stuck with prices on a par with slab, but without slab's productivity advantage.

In all, in 1882, the 36 quarries of Caernarfonshire employed 8960 men, sold just under 281,000 tons averaging 31 tons per man, with a per man revenue of £76.00. But ignoring the 3 top performers, Penrhyn, Dinorwig and Dorothea, the 2859 men in the rest of the county produced 65,500 tons, less than 23 tons per man. Although most got around £2.45 per ton, many can have been scarcely covering their wage bills.

At Nantlle, Coed Madoc beset with water problems (pumping was costing £100 per month) closed their Gloddfa Glai pit. The small Cloddfa'r Coed closed completely. Even Pen y Bryn, only recently employing over 250 men, was faltering and would shortly close. Closures at Nantlle were liable to be permanent as leases of idle working were quickly snapped up by neighbours as dumps for rubbish. There had been a proposal for a co-operatively funded railway to dump into the sea near Pontllyfni but like a similar scheme to collectively drain and pump, the slump killed off such ideas. Many of the family workings, on tiny sites with no rail connection, had closed. Once there had been well over 40 undertakings at Nantlle, now amalgamation and closure had reduced this to about 15. According to a contemporary report, only 3 of these were breaking even. In 1884 even Dorothea's profits would be seriously dented when water broke in, drowning 7 men, (believed to be the most serious single accident in a Welsh slate quarry), and they eventually had to spend £30,000 on remedial work.

In the Llangollen & Glynceiriog area in 1876 there had been 8 quarries with about 600 men producing nearly 20,000 tons. In 1882 only 3 quarries were open, their 160 men raising less than 4000 tons. Everywhere quarries were closing, some never to reopen. In this rigid climate, only the most efficient could survive.

During the next few years many undertakings, particularly those with poor transport, would close. Some small and marginal, such as the 7 man Bwlch y Ddwy Elor, but also larger ones like Cedryn and its associated Cwmeigiau, who in spite of (or rather because of) the big sums expended, gave up trying to triumph over their difficulties. For similar reasons Hafod y Llan closed. A host of openings or re-openings of the heady 60s and 70s failed. Not that good transport necessarily brought success, for Corris with its newly steamed railway suffered as badly as anywhere and quarries such as Abercwmeiddaw would succumb. Unhappily too, the great prosperity brought to the quarries to the south of Llanberis by the railway, proved short lived. Some closed, others operated on a reduced scale, and Gallt y Llan at Nant Peris finally succumbed to poor rock and their distance from the railway.

At Blaenau in 1882 about 4000 men in 20 or so quarries raised something over 130,000 tons, with revenues per man averaging around £100. However with the Welsh Slate Company achieving perhaps £150, and Llechwedd over £130, returns at some others, especially those with heavy coal bills, must have been less than rosy. The statement made at the time that of the 15 quarries in Blaenau, only 4 were profitable, may well have been correct.

Whatever their troubles, few quarries would suffer problems as serious as W.S.C. Pressing to increase productivity to compensate for lower sales and lower prices, they took a reckless approach to working practices. Their sales had peaked at near 50,000 tons in 1875, by 1882 they were down to under 35,000 tons, but by cutting corners, they achieved this with a workforce almost halved to little more than 700, an astonishing near 50 tons per man, way ahead of Llechwedd whose consistent 40 plus tons of large, top-quality roofing slate was regarded as an industry best. W.S.C. probably reduced the pillar width to less than the proper 30', always a temptation, as the pillars represented good, easily worked rock. They certainly failed to take proper care to precisely align their chambers with those of Mathew's and Holland's which were above them. It was alleged that they did their measuring with a *'Three-foot walking stick'!*. They had been prosecuted in 1874 for failing to keep proper plans of their workings. Since they were only fined 2/6 (12.5p), risking further penalties must have seemed a better bet than employing a surveyor! In December 1882 the inevitable happened and there was a serious fall. Two months later, whilst management was still figuring out how to get the affected district re-started, another, much bigger fall occurred. Reputedly over six million tons of rock came down, all but destroying much of the quarry, (fortunately without causing any injury).

Considerable damage was done to Mathew's and to Holland's. These were now in W.E. Oakeley's hands. Having managed the estate for some years on behalf of his aunt, W.G. Oakeley's widow, he had finally inherited in 1878. Not content with his handsome royalty income, he wanted the quarry profits as well, so one of his first actions was to decline to renew the leases on these two quarries. With the help of loans from Rock Insurance and bankers and C. Hoare & Co, he bought them out. Running them proved no easy task, as Mathew's in particular, in anticipation of having to give up possession, had been operated with a regrettable concentration on short time profit. Also it was now apparent that he had entered an industry just as it was poised for a downturn.

With his two quarries damaged and facing the prospect of a serious diminution of the royalties from W.S.C. which were urgently needed to service his loans and pay for his extensions to Plas Tan y Bwlch, Mr Oakeley was not a happy man. He eventually won a protracted legal action against Welsh Slate but since there was no chance of his £110,000 compensation award being paid, he seized their quarry and set about running the three as a single unit.

Cwmorthin had furiously pushed their annual output into five figures, also partly by pillar-robbing. In 1884 the inevitable happened and there was a major collapse, not on the W.S.C. scale but enough to render almost half the workings unusable. A subsequent examination by Thomas Jones, Oakeley's engineer, found *'pillars less than 10 feet thick instead of the proper 30 feet'*. In fairness it must be said that such practice, and that of 'cupboarding' (cutting recesses in pillars) was quite widespread. Nor was it confined to the 19thC. West Llangynog closed in 1937 due to a collapse caused by pillar robbing to meet an urgent order.

The fall broke the Cwmorthin company. The quarry was reopened in 1889 by the New Welsh Slate Company, a re-incarnation of the old W.S.C. They never prospered and eventually in 1900 Oakeley, by then operating as a limited company, took them over. In all, Oakeley would ultimately have 12 mills containing 500 saw tables, would have almost 50 miles of rail track, and 11 miles of compressed airline. But for all its size, Oakeley, like other Blaenau quarries, would never again replicate the profits of the 60s and 70s.

In 1883 the market remained weak. Some Caernarfonshire quarries held up fairly well but the brunt fell on north Meirionnydd, where competition in the export market forced further cutbacks in output. Production fell by around 10% (about half due to W.S.C.'s problems), but more seriously, their revenues dropped by a full 15%[1].

By 1884 prices of even the best slates were 30% or more below the 1876 peak and by 1886 the total Welsh tonnage had fallen to less than 400,000. Imports which had been encouraged by the recent high prices took an increasing market share. Besides the traditional European sources, slate was now also coming from the United States, where many quarries were worked by Welshmen who had emigrated during previous depressions[2], even taking with them such place names as Bangor.

This fall in trade was accompanied by an entirely new factor. No longer could the employers arbitrarily cut wages and lay of 'hands', since in 1874, following the frustration by some owners of earlier attempts, the North Wales Quarrymen's Union had been formed.

Unionism came late to the slate quarries, as revolutionary theories which had found ready support in English mills and manufactories, did not readily take root in a culture more versed in the Mabinogion than in Marx. The various uprisings, both agricultural and industrial which had occurred in south and mid Wales earlier in the century, had no counterparts in the north. The chapel rather than a union or a political movement was the instinctive focus of solidarity. And a strong focus it was, chapel loyalties were fervent and remained so in rural areas up to the mid 20thC. Their influence was formidable, forming an alternative society, with a rigid hierarchy of the minister, (who might well be an ex-quarryman), deacons and other officers, who carried great moral authority among their congregations. Though sharing a common dissension from the Established Church, rivalry between differing chapels, even those of the same denomination was fierce. It was possibly on the realisation that chapel loyalties were too disparate (there were well over 30 chapels in Blaenau Ffestiniog alone) to effectively further their interests, which caused the men to turn to unionism.

Unsurprisingly, the NWQMU was largely a Penrhyn and Dinorwig initiative. Both proprietors had shown a degree of concern for the welfare of their workers by the building of hospitals, schools etc. and in the provision of (small) pensions and so on. But they had always run their quarries in an authoritarian style, with scant regard for Chwarae Teg (fair play) so innate in the Welsh people. They are said for instance, to have paid higher wages to churchgoing men, and they certainly ignored the favouritism and corruption rife amongst their letting stewards and middle managers. In fact it was probably dissatisfaction with such unfairnesses rather than pay and conditions that was foremost in the minds of the union founders.

Most of the other big quarries were run by owners, who whilst not always totally benevolent towards their employees, understood them better, many sharing their Liberal and Chapel views. Also Penrhyn and Dinorwig were both virtually monopolistic employers in their respective areas. Whereas in such places as Blaenau and Nantlle there were opportunities for dissatisfied men to find work in other quarries, particularly in the buoyant middle 70s.

A contemporary report in the *Caernarvon and Denbigh Herald* remarked on '*The better feeling in Blaenau quarries as opposed to Caernarvonshire due to the Liberal and Non-conformist sympathies of the owners and the speaking of Welsh by the superintendents, as well as to better wages*'. The benevolence of management was instanced by citing '*The provision of a Pudding Room[3] by Mr Percival*' (of Votty and Bowydd). They also went on to say that '*The men of Blaenau are less given to drinking and debauchery, than those elsewhere*'(*!*)

Certainly in the smaller quarries such as many in Nantlle, the 'them and us' comprised not so much masters versus men, as both, collectively, versus the big neighbouring quarries. The Darbishires of Pen yr Orsedd actively welcomed the formation of a union, and there were even some Nantlle owners who held office in the NWQMU. These factors were reflected in the figures for union membership which by 1878 totalled 8000. At Penrhyn over 90% joined and at Dinorwig about 83%. yet in Nantlle only 25% were unionists and at Blaenau scarcely 10%.

There was, almost unique to the slate industry, a further ingredient to complicate industrial relations. Most men being Bargainers and many also working their own small-holdings, they thought of themselves as independent contractors and viewed any classification as 'Wage-slaves' to be demeaning. Also there was, at least until latter years, the absence of a 'craft' element whereby skilled men sought to distance themselves from the lesser skilled, and to protect 'differentials'. Rockmen made common cause with their Rubblers and Labourers, to whom they were probably related, shared the same Caban and undoubtedly attended the same chapel.

There was also the problem of Language and Nationality. Apart from the actual difficulty of communication, many English owners and managers tended to have a 'Colonial' outlook, seeing themselves as bringing civilisation to these natives who spoke only in an unintelligible tongue[4]. On the other hand the 'natives' would have little esteem for persons ignorant of the 'Language of Heaven' and its accompanying culture.

The NWQMU operated in an unusual industry and was itself unusual. Normally when a union was formed, officials were elected from among the members and often held more extreme views and possibly were less devoted to the work ethic, than the men they represented. Initially the leaders of the NWQMU were not quarrymen, mainly because acceptance of office would have meant dismissal, but partly because it was wished to have men of standing and negotiating experience. The first president J.L. Jones, was the owner of several small quarries, and also prominent were a bank manager, a doctor and several schoolteachers. The general secretary, later president, W.J. Parry was the son of a quarryman but had built up a substantial business, describing himself as a *'Builder's Merchant, Oil, Powder and Dynamite Merchant and Implement and Quarry Tool Agent'*. He also had accountancy qualifications and was Agent to the Cenfaes Estate. W.J. Williams who succeeded Parry as secretary, was a practising professional accountant. An unlikely assembly perhaps, but Parry in particular would prove an outstanding leader, his total bilingualism invaluable in dealing with management.

Immediately following the formation of the union there had been a clash at Glynrhonwy. Membership was prohibited and when the men ignored this injunction they were locked out. With demand for slate brisk and alternative work available at other quarries, this caused more problems for management than for the men. Within 3 weeks the quarry was reopened, with union membership tacitly tolerated. Shortly afterwards there was trouble at Dinorwig. Thomas Assheton-Smith the second had died in 1858 leaving the estate to his ten year old nephew, George W. Duff. When young George attained his majority in 1869 he assumed the Assheton-Smith name and set about sorting things at the quarry. By 1874 his various tinkerings including alterations to the payment structure, had generated a lot of ill-will. His men walked out, when they returned five weeks later, it was substantially on their own terms.

The big test came at Penrhyn. Colonel Douglas-Pennant had been ennobled in 1866 and reviving his predecessor's Irish title, was now First Baron Penrhyn of Llandegai. Colonel or lord, he was still the man to beat, and beat him they did.

The actual cause of the 1874 Penrhyn dispute was not about wages although there was considerable discontent over the pay structure, distortions of which meant that good workers producing much first-class material might be worse off than less able or less diligent men making little more than rubble. Nor was it directly union related, but merely a trifling tiff over a collection made in working time. Such collections were commonplace whether for distressed colleagues or for wider causes, such as those made towards the establishment of Universities at Aberystwyth and Bangor, but this one was in aid of the Dinorwig strikers, which to his lordship was a definite no-no. The dispute grew into a full blown stand-off, which lasted over two months but resulted in a shake out of senior management and in the signing of the

Pennant-Lloyd agreement (named after the Penrhyn Estate Agent). This 1874 agreement was a landmark not so much because it improved and codified the working conditions, gave the men some voice in the running of the quarry and acknowledged the need for a minimum wage, but because its very signing recognised for the first time, delegates' rights to negotiate on behalf of the men.

During the rest of the 1870s, there were few serious disputes, the only major one being at Rhos in 1877, which although it lasted two whole bitter years, was purely a local matter. But when the downturn started to bite at the end of that decade, bringing wage cuts and lay-offs, there was more general trouble, particularly at the less profitable but strongly unionised quarries at Llanberis and Nantlle. From 1879 on, there were strikes at Cook & Ddol, Goodman's, Cambrian, Glynrhonwy Upper, Cefn Du, Cilgwyn, Braich, Alexandra, Pen yr Orsedd and Moel Tryfan. At Bryn Hafod y Wern, there were 4 strikes in seven years. There were wage reductions and lay-offs at the larger Caernarfonshire quarries such as Dorothea, Penrhyn and Dinorwig, but these were generally less drastic and were negotiated without serious confrontation. Blaenau quarries with their greater profitability, were less affected as they could pay above Caernarfonshire rates, which by the mid 80s, in the smaller quarries, were at best 4/3 (21p) per day, with for instance Cilgwyn paying under 4/ (20p) for top men. Penrhyn was paying up to 5/ (25p) per day but even this contrasted with the 7/6 (37.5p) some men had been getting a few years before.

No union could fight harsh economic facts, there was disenchantment with this route to betterment and membership dropped away, falling to well under 3000 by 1884. The men increasingly turned back to their chapels as a focus of solidarity.

From 1880 at Dinorwig, things started to go really sour. W.W. Vivian was appointed general manager, his success in commerce (and his being the son of a peer?), apparently overriding his lack of experience of controlling a large workforce and his ignorance of quarrying. He was charged with the task of improving the profitability of the quarry, which had always failed to match Penrhyn's performance. This was mainly because of geological problems, with bad rock having been worked around rather than boldly removed. Rubbish had been dumped with little forethought and something of a hotchpotch had developed, particularly in the Allt Ddu/Chwarel Fawr districts. Also Penrhyn tended to get better prices, more perhaps due to their agents' skilful marketing, than any superiority of product. These difficulties Vivian could in the short term do little about. To try to get more out of the men was something he could and did tackle. There were five years of mounting tension and dissension, but no actual conflict.

Reference has been made to the close connection with the land by the quarrymen, particularly those of north Caernarfonshire. This was in fact a carry-over from the old metal mine practice of farm hands working part-time. Thus the custom of taking days off or of leaving work early, to attend to their own holdings or to help neighbours with theirs, was strongly ingrained. As Bargainers, which most of the men were, they saw nothing wrong in this. If they chose to sacrifice earnings, they felt that only they were the losers. A manager such as Vivian trying to maximise output, by running things on factory-like lines, with hours governed by the hooter, viewed matters differently. Thus much dissension was attendance-related.

As is usual in such matters, a small event was the spark which turned discontent into disorder. In addition to the regular quarry holidays, it had become usual for the men to take a day off at the end of the 4-week month. When in 1885 some of the Dinorwig men, observing this tacit custom, were ordered back to work, resentment built up. Shortly after this when men were seen by an under-manager, waiting for the hooter not at their workplaces, but at the edge of the quarry site, a whole gallery was suspended. Although Vivian did not fully support his under-manager, he did not completely rescind the suspension. Following further disputes about working on the last day of the month, and the holding of meetings on quarry property, there was a Lock-out.

Fifteen weeks of idleness followed, with some negotiation, much bitterness, a little vandalism, but no violence. There were even elements of farce. There was much glee when Assheton-Smith was prosecuted for winging a beater whilst out shooting. The Dinorwig Band, when ordered to surrender their instruments, (which as with most of the numerous quarry bands were provided by the owners), very publicly played them as they marched in to return them. Then, finding no-one at the quarry who would accept them, marched home again, much to the delight of onlookers.

Eventually, largely due to the intervention of John Robinson, the owner of Tal y Sarn, the men were persuaded to return. The terms were substantially those dictated by Vivian, rules would not be relaxed, new working practices would be introduced and manning would be cut by some 500.

The shortage caused by the Dinorwig shut-down helped prices to firm a little for 1886, and with some improvement in trade during the latter part of the 80s they were by 1889 around 5% up on the low of 1884/85. Although still a full 25% less than the 1876 peak, there was now a little more scope for managements to be flexible and conflict to an extent receded. At Blaenau trade was good and confidence was returning, as demonstrated by the Greaves' in 1887 further extending their Llechedd holding, by leasing from the Rev. Haygarth part of Friddybach[5].

Nantlle too, was busy, although some quarries such as Coed Madoc had declined and the likes of Brynfferam and Fron were on almost nominal outputs, Pen yr Orsedd had almost restored its manning to the 400 it had been in the 1860s. Cilgwyn's 318 and Tal y Sarn's 360 payrolls were almost their best and Dorothea's 550 was their highest ever. Alexandra was doing well with 230 men, South Dorothea had a remarkable 104 and Cloddfa'r Coed an incredible 150, equalling Moel Tryfan's total. Several of the intermittently worked smaller diggings were revived.

On the other hand, at Penrhyn serious and portentous events were taking place. In 1885, Lord Penrhyn, now a sick 85 year old (he died the following year), passed control to his son, George Sholto Gordon Douglas Pennant. The heir, pushing 50, having spent most of his adult life watching his inheritance grow, had lately seen decline threaten. Undoubtedly spurred by his close friend Emilius Alexander Young, one of the company's auditors, he had smouldered, impatient to remedy what he perceived as his father's senilities, and Wyatt, the manager's, weaknesses.

The new master immediately arranged for Wyatt to retire 'due to ill-health', and over the heads of better qualified applicants, appointed Young in his place. Young was at once able to show that his predecessor had been lax in his accounting and by this means confirmed his employer's confidence in him. Young may have been a competent manager of figures but as a manager of men he was definitely less than outstanding. His deficiencies would soon become apparent and it is puzzling why, in the ensuing years, he continued to enjoy the new Lord Penrhyn's backing for his so often unwise policies.

The Penrhyn/Young team was encouraged by the decline in the strength of the Union, for the NWQMU was both in membership and its influence on affairs, a shadow of what it had been a decade before. They, with some justification, felt that the Pennant-Lloyd Agreement had handed too much influence in the running of the quarry to the men, but instead of seeking to re-negotiate, flatly repudiated it. The new policy was to run the quarry with a 'firm hand'. Transgressions that would have previously warranted a warning now resulted in suspensions, with an especial crack-down on 'union activities'. Thus there followed at Penrhyn a decade of discontent.

[1] Examples of cutbacks 1882-1883

	1882		1883	
Abercwmeiddaw	4173	188	2875	180
Alexandra	4550	195	3721	182
Cefn Du	5640	197	4040	172
Cilgwyn	7430	300	4956	215
Cwt y Bugail	2459	73	1662	40
Deeside	1105	42	600	34
Dinorwig	87429	2757	85000	2710
Dorothea	16598	533	15841	481
Fronheulog	1642	98	1364	69
Graig Ddu	3140	110	807	36
Minllyn	2830	108	1468	71
Moel Tryfan	1880	81	1781	70
Penrhyn	111166	2889	110382	2838
Penrhyngwyn	250	47	54	20
Prince Llywelyn	1685	74	1315	42
Ratgoed	434	15	382	8
Rhos	1285	45	1005	40
Wrysgan	2078	96	1396	51

(A full list of 1883 outputs and manning is in appendix 3)

[2] A report in the Mining Journal of 1869 mentions difficulties in several Pennsylvania quarries due to the widespread use of the Welsh language. The 4 men gangs replicated Welsh methods. Productivity close to 50 tons per man year, doubtless reflected more easily won rock. Although selling prices were on a par, wages coming out at 40p-60p per day were by Welsh standards attractive. The same report mentioned Writing Slates, 1000 per day being made by one man cutting and two men 'smoothing'.

[3] The 'Pudding' was rice pudding, this being one of several benevolent efforts to improve nutrition by encouraging milk consumption. This same benevolence (beside Temperance considerations) also led to the Cocoa Rooms at Blaenau (now the RWF club).

[4] The 1901 Census recorded that in Bethesda, out of a population of 5281, 3152 were recorded as monoglot Welsh. And the figure of 2091 claiming bilingualism, is undoubtedly an exaggeration, as many with the barest smattering of English would undoubtedly have boasted of the accomplishment.

[5] This increased their number of landlords to 3, the others being Lord Newborough and the Oakeley family. For royalty purposes, separate accounts of tonnages would have to be accurately maintained for each. This was a burden on several quarries whose holdings derived from more than one lease. Indeed when Tan yr Allt closed in 1879 this was partly because of problems of apportioning dues between 4 landowners.

9. Triumph and Tragedy
The 1890s

By 1890 the fragile recovery of the previous couple of years was faltering and price lists were trimmed [1]. Tonnage at 410,000, was better than it had been, but was still nearly 40,000 less than late 70s peak. A year later output was below 400,000 tons, and manning at under 13,000, was almost 2000 down. Much of the drop fell on Nantlle, where by 1891 several of the smaller workings had closed and at others manning was slashed and wages cut. Penrhyn and Dinorwig retrenched and even booming Blaenau was affected. Diffwys failed and although it was restarted, it never recovered its former eminence.

A couple of years into the decade an upturn in the building industry brought a renewed demand for slate. By 1894, this had become almost a stampede. In spite of production being lost by the freezing weather at the end of the year, outputs were nudging previous records. Everywhere there was a turnaround, Nantlle more than regained its lost trade, Blaenau resumed its climb. Several quarries such as Penarth which had failed to keep open in the recent slack times, restarted. Attempts at new openings were renewed although the chances of finding new, workable rock were slim. Typical of these was Ffynnon Badarn, near Corris, where optimistically, a tramway was planned to reach a trifling outcrop hundreds of feet up a cliff.

There was success south of the Dyfi estuary. For many years some slate had been dug there, but there was now more serious activity. Glandyfi was busy supplying slab for enamelling at Aberystwyth, and there were new openings at Morben and at Tyn y Garth as well as some smaller diggings. Their combined outputs briefly reached several thousand tons, but they would become early casualties when the slab market declined.

By 1896 prices not only stood at a remarkable 25-30% above those of 1890, but held for 3 years. Even when trade eased a little in 1899, lists were still above anything seen since 1878.

However the 90s were most notable, not for the trade recovery, but for three portentous events; the Llechwedd stoppage of 1893, the publication in 1895 of the Report of the Enquiry into the Meirionethshire Mines and the Penrhyn stoppage of 1896-7. All leading up to the cataclysm of 1900.

To deal with the Mines Report first. Although the enquiry's remit was confined to the underground workings of the one county, it served to publicise the dangers and hardships in slate quarrying generally. Although the Chairman Sir Charles Foster (as he later became) was above suspicion, much of the evidence was not, being provided by understandably biased management, and by employees fearful of their jobs. More flagrant was the evidence of medical men employed by, or on retainers from the quarry owners. Whilst the standard of medical attention given by quarry doctors was invariably of the best, their impartiality when matters of compensation were involved, was often questionable. The term 'Natural causes' was sometimes elastic, and 'Visitations of God' on such devout communities were surprisingly frequent. For this reason there were recurrent moves to put sick clubs outside of quarry control, or to permit opting out of membership, so that medical opinion independent of quarry influence could be obtained.

In spite of this, the report made clear how unhealthy and hazardous slate quarrying was. It showed that even though there were no disasters from explosive or asphyxiating gas, it was more dangerous to work in an underground slate quarry, than even the most notorious of coal mines. Roofs crumbling, falling rock, blocks slipping during handling, missed footings in the dark, stumblings near the many sheer drops, running down by waggons — there were a hundred dangers. It was scarcely safer in the open quarries. Wet, greasy rock, and precipitous pits reached by rickety ladders, presented additional hazards. In all workings there were winches and hand cranes whose ratchets slipped, sending winding handles spinning to kill or maim. Blasting had been made safer by the obligatory provision of blast shelters, and by firing at fixed times with bugle and flag warnings, but accidents from shot firing were still commonplace.

At the smaller, remoter quarries, an injured man could be a very long way and a very long time, from medical attention of any kind. At some of the larger quarries his chances might be better. Besides the hospitals at Penrhyn, Dinorwig and Oakeley, other owners at Blaenau Ffestiniog had put the town ahead of many municipalities by sponsoring a hospital in 1848. These institutions were competently staffed and by the standards of the time well equipped, founding a tradition of care which the hospitals of north Wales still ably continue. Indeed Penrhyn hospital was a pioneer in the use of anaesthetics, and Dinorwig in the development of X-Rays and amputation prostheses. However it could still be a lengthy and painful journey for a patient to reach them from distant workplaces. Thus fractures and other injuries not ordinarily life-threatening, could result in death, or at best, permanent disablement.

The report drew attention to the chronically bad diet of the men, although this was passed off as a *'failure by the wives to provide proper meals'*. It highlighted the great incidence of diseases, particularly pulmonary complaints, some 50% of male deaths being from respiratory causes. These some witnesses attributed not to dust, damp and bad housing, but to *'drinking stewed tea'*[2] The report also drew attention to the awful conditions prevailing in barracks, and the plight of men who having walked many miles in rain to work, would spend the day in wet clothes, either on exposed open rock faces, draughty sheds or in watery conditions underground. Thus deaths, or serious disability from disease, were even more numerous than those from traumatic causes. Added to which, even in the large quarries with sick pay schemes, economic necessity could force an ill or injured man to return to work before recovery was complete. For all its faults the report was a damning condemnation of conditions in the industry.

The Llechwedd strike of 1893 was the first ever serious dispute at Blaenau Ffestiniog, and indeed was to be the only one of any consequence for almost a century to come. Unionism still found little favour at Blaenau, with only about a quarter of the men belonging, (and many of these in arrears with their dues!). Over the years there had been occasional brief strikes, but disputes were invariably settled quickly, amicably and without rancour. The managers who were virtually all local men with a sound quarrying background, were always ready to listen to and act on, genuine grievances properly presented. Blaenau owners too, were for the most part realistic over concessions.

When trade took an upturn in 1892 a wage increase was sought, although the basic 5/- (25p) per day which was granted at the end of the year, was not far short of the men's expectations, some dissatisfaction remained. This dissatisfaction was strongest at Llechwedd, where undoubtedly due to the increased wage costs, the Greaves brothers (sons of J.W. who had retired in 1870 and died in 1880), felt the need to tighten up on working practices. Also due to the constraints of water-supply, some men had to work on a 'split-shift' basis which involved them in unpaid waiting time. J.E. Greaves did not help matters by dismissing the discontent as being merely due to *'Union activities'*. In May of 1893, when a man allegedly finishing early was ordered back to work, 486 men, almost all of the workforce, walked out. The strike lasted 16 acrimonious weeks before the men came back, having gained few concessions.

The 1896-7 Penrhyn dispute was to prove a more serious matter, and its effects would spread far beyond that one quarry. The seeds had been sown in the previous decade or two, in 1896 they sprouted. Not that the germination was without nurture, for Young, motivated by a profit sharing contract, pursued a drive for ever greater efficiency, suspending, sacking and abrogating long-tolerated practices. Much resented was his introduction of outside contractors to clear waste and rubble. Exception was also taken to the appointment of 'Safety Inspectors' who were perceived as management spies.

There was growing disenchantment amongst many of the men with the Union. National politics increasingly impinged on its affairs. The widening of the franchise in 1884, having ended the Tory landowner's grip on Council and Parliamentary seats, it was felt that Union officials were using their positions to further personal political ambitions. Their position, vis-a-vis management was questioned, even W.J. Parry, being heavily dependent on his supply contracts with the quarry, suffered some mistrust. (This anomaly being corrected when Young, alleging overcharging, ceased to do business with him.) Increasingly, politicians were also seen as exploiting the problems of the industry in general and Penrhyn in particular for self-advertisement.

On several occasions during the 90s there had been times when management's intransigence, might have met with more robust responses but a combination of confusion and indifference averted any positive action by the Penrhyn men.

The appointment of D.R. Daniel in 1896 as full-time organiser, put Union matters on a firmer footing, and in fact a strike was planned for 1897, should the demands for wage increases and so on not be met, (by which time Union finances were expected to be in better shape). However in September 1896 these plans were overtaken by events. A number of men were suspended for having taken a day off to attend a rally. A complete stoppage ensued.

The Union was too ill-funded to offer much support but many men were able to find other work. Some were taken on by other slate or granite quarries, others by the contractors then building the Snowdon Mountain Railway, and the waterworks at Lake Vyrnwy. A number left the area for good. It was August 1897 before there was an agreement to return to work. The Union claimed that '*Substantial concessions*' had been won, but Young's view that he had '*obtained complete victory on every point*', was probably a more accurate assessment of the outcome.

With the 1897 Penrhyn dispute settled, and management's right to manage apparently vindicated, the industry forged ahead. Blaenau's growth found a new impetus and Nantlle positively boomed, Pen yr Orsedd alone employing 450 and turning out 13,741 tons. In the north-east, Moelfferna's manning leapt to almost 200, four times their total less than a decade earlier.

Again there was a spate of new but usually hopeless diggings. At remote Cwm Du there was an attempt to make a fresh opening and many fruitless holes were tunnelled as in the Arthog area. Maes y

Gamfa, full of hope, built a connection to the Hendre Ddu tramway.

By 1898 tonnage for the Welsh industry reached an unprecedented half million, with manning nearing 17,000, but a close look at the statistics might have given pause for thought. Penrhyn and Dinorwig did not fully share this growth and in some quarries output actually fell, Votty & Bowydd's 1898 figures being well short of their 17000 tons of 1897. Generally however, the prospects for the New Year of 1899 looked bright, the slight difficulties at the Cape having caused no problems to the industry. But as it became clear that Boer farmers were running rings round the British Army, business confidence was affected, Bank Rate rose, the building industry faltered and orders fell off. There was concern, but little serious worry as the industry was well accustomed to temporary setbacks.

In early 1900 continuing bad war news kept trade flat. Following the national euphoria in May at the relief of Mafeking, there came reports of British advances. These and a repeat defeat of the Liberals at the polls meant that towards the end of the year, business optimism was widespread. The slate trade could look forward to an imminent return to growth.

Then came the second great stoppage at Penrhyn.

It is difficult to make any comment on the 1900-1903 cessation of work without immediately taking sides. It has been called a Strike , it has been called a Lock-Out, and even now, in parts of Bethesda, it may still be wise to be wary of which term one uses. But whichever term one does use, it was immediately apparent that 1897, serious though it was, had merely been a trailer of the main event.

To pursue the same analogy, the scenario was now somewhat different. The conciliatory W.J. Williams, the Union secretary, had resigned as had the president, the able W.J. Parry. The old team of outside men, whose interests embraced the Radical cause on a broad basis, had been replaced by quarrymen, whose interests were more narrowly focused on the industry. They were men who perceived that a quarter of a century's persuasion had achieved little, and that a more vigorous and militant approach was called for. Not all the men approved this change of emphasis, which caused some further disenchantment with the Union. This apparent decline in the support for the Union and its leadership did not escape the notice of management.

In 1899, a trivial incident had occurred, which whilst illustrating the delicacy of relations, also tells us something of the men's character. Lord Penrhyn made it known that he would refuse to allow his daughter (one of twelve!) to accept a wedding present from the men, apparently because the collection had been organised by the Union. This caused resentment out of all proportion to its importance. Even more inflammatory was Young's edict at the end of the year that Bangor Fair days would no longer be holidays.

Young was on a high, the quarry showed a profit of nearly £120,000 in 1899, of which his share was over £3,500, enabling him to live in a style to which he was rapidly becoming accustomed. (He employed 4 domestic servants, 2 nursemaids and a governess, he had a yacht and in 1899 boasted that certain of his investments had increased in value by £30,000). That year his second-in-command D. Pritchard fell ill and had to retire. Whilst never disloyal, Pritchard had been a moderating influence on some of Young's worst excesses. His successor was H.P. Meares who having been an engineer in India, was well accustomed to dealing with 'native labour' and who had no intention of being a moderating influence on anybody. Thus backed, Young introduced various economies such as reducing the rate of new pensions, from 7/6 (37.5p) to 5/- (25p) per week, and restricting them to *necessitous men of good character*. It is said that he dismissed for alleged misconduct, several senior men nearing retirement to avoid paying them pensions. When it became apparent early in 1900 that profits (and hence his cut) were likely to be down, his attitude became draconian. In April, knowing that the Union was short of funds, he forbade the collection of union dues on quarry property. A measure, which having regard to the wide scattering of the men's homes, should have made continued collection almost impossible.

Far from harming the union, this edict had the unexpected effect of causing a flood of men to join or re-join.

Throughout the Summer of 1900 there was friction at Penrhyn not only between management and men, but also between the men seen as accepting the rigid regime and those who resisted it. In October, there was trouble in a gallery where there had previously been disputes and suspensions over lettings. Violence broke out, quarry property was damaged and a man was injured. The next month there were further disturbances, resulting in police intervention. Twenty six men were prosecuted and although eighteen were acquitted, all were dismissed. The magistrates fearing trouble, sought military assistance, but when a large number of quarrymen abandoned work to march to Bangor in support of their victimised colleagues, there were no incidents. Management responded to this absenteeism by suspending the whole quarry for two weeks, at the end of which time, when Bargains were re-let, a number of men were not offered work. Almost all of the near 3000 workforce walked out, and the quarry gates were shut behind them. This was neither a strike or a lock-out, it was war. The issues were complex, but the men's grievances were aptly summarised at the time by Richard Greaves of Llechwedd as — 'The contract system, the manager's lack of practical experience and a general nostalgia for the times when things were slackly run'.

The Radical London press took an immediate interest and dispatched reporters, making the dispute a matter of country-wide debate. In fact in December, when the first real discussions took place between the Union and management, they were brought together largely by the efforts of Clement Edwards, a Daily News journalist[3]. At these discussions management did offer some concessions, which were so trivial that the men rejected them out of hand.

Increasingly, prominent Radical politicians such as David Lloyd George identified themselves with the dispute, but how much this was due to a real concern for the issues, or how much it was an opportunity to get personal press coverage is not clear. Certainly, attempts were made to couple support for the Penrhyn men with opposition to the South African war, likening the quarrymen to the Boer farmers, a comparison which both parties would doubtless have hotly repudiated. Matters remained relatively quiet for some months, with the quarry at a standstill. In June 1901 when Lord Penrhyn reopened the gates offering work to all those who would accept his terms, about 400 men opted to do so. Resentment was fanned by a rumour that these men received a sovereign each from his Lordship personally and allegedly, an increase in wages. Events now took a more serious turn, there were periodic disturbances, 'Y Bradwyr' (The Traitors) and their families, were threatened, troops were again called in and arrests made.

New Year's Eve brought the first ugliness, there were violent clashes and troops were deployed in strength. Such scenes were not repeated, but throughout the whole of 1902 there was stalemate. Lord Penrhyn refused to deal with what he called 'deputations' and hardened his attitude, all attempts at arbitration failing. There were evictions from quarry-owned cottages, occupied by strikers or men who had obtained work elsewhere, the properties being re-let to 'loyal' men. Messages of approval for Lord Penrhyn came from many quarters, Assheton-Smith of Dinorwig being understandably one of his warmest supporters. This support did not however prevent him from poaching Penrhyn's customers, and taking on Penrhyn men, increasing his workforce to over 3000. By 1903 Penrhyn affairs had become a subject of parliamentary debate, but more as a stick for Liberal members to beat Tory landowners in general, rather than quarry owners in particular, which further clouded the local issues.

In April that year Lord Penrhyn won a libel action against W.J. Parry. The previous year Parry had re-opened Pantdreiniog quarry providing work for 50 men, a costly enterprise which together with the libel costs, the loss of his Penrhyn contracts and a serious fire at his yard, almost bankrupted him. Whilst Parry no longer held office he still very much epitomized the men's cause and his setbacks were seen as a moral gain for Lord Penrhyn. Union funds, meagre from the start, and although substantially augmented by other workers' movements and public appeals, were dwindling.

On the other hand, the quarry was doing relatively well, the workforce augmented by outside men, such as lead miners, had edged up to 1100, and with the bargain teams reduced from four to three, unprecedented productivity was claimed. (By concentrating the reduced workforce on easily worked faces, postponing maintenance and suspending all development, higher than normal tonnages per man could well have resulted.) This enabled management to refuse to countenance any talk of full re-engagement, it being claimed that not above 2000 would be required for full-scale working. By late 1903 the Union with outside support fading was fighting a rearguard action, with fewer than 600 men actually on strike. On 7th November with an increasing number of men applying to be taken back, a vote to end the strike was passed by a small majority.

The men were utterly defeated, the village was demoralised, even the chapels so central to the quarrymen's solidarity, lost much of their influence. The pre-eminence of Bethesda in the affairs of the industry evaporated. Within 4 years Lord Penrhyn was dead, within 5 years the NWQMU, with Penrhyn membership at an all-time low had, with the appointment of R.T. Jones as its sole full-time official, become Blaenau Ffestiniog centred.

Besides those moving to other slate districts, 200 Bethesda men had emigrated, a similar number had found work outside the industry, many going to the collieries of south Wales, (where their skill with timbering and general adaptability, was much sought after). Those that remained and all their counterparts in other quarries would find themselves in very changed circumstances in the years to come.

[1] List prices were one thing, invoiced prices another. An 1890 Aberllefenni Price Card exists which shows overwritten reductions of up to 5/- (25p) per ton on some of the thinner (ie, more expensive) slab. Also inked in are discounts of 17½ less 10%, less 2½%. So that for what was almost their top slab product, listed at £4 per ton, they were quoting only £2.71.

[2] Even in the 1920s, slate dust was being described as 'beneficial'. It was not until the 1930s that dust extraction and dust suppression was seriously tackled and dust-induced lung diseases were recognised as compensatable complaints, for which employers could be sued. Since by this time many employers had gone out of business, victims were denied any source of redress. It was not until 1979 that a Government scheme was enacted to grant such men, or such few of them who were then still surviving, appropriate compensation.

[3] Some aspects of these happenings were related to the author by Clement Edwards' daughter, when he had the pleasure of accompanying her on her first visit to Penrhyn quarry, over 80 years afterwards.

10. The Great Decline
The 1900s

It is said that the industry never recovered from the Penrhyn dispute. Indeed the start of its steep and ultimately near-terminal decline coincided with that calamitous stoppage, but the decline largely arose from other causes. At most the Penrhyn events accelerated a contraction which external factors had already made inevitable.

The peak year of output was 1898, thus by the time the Penrhyn gates were shut, demand for Welsh slate was already falling. Although the late 1890s had seemed a boom era, in fact Welsh slate's share of the total potential market decreased. By the year 1895 imported tonnages had reached an unprecedented 20,000, and whilst the shortages and price rises during the Penrhyn stoppage gave them a further boost, this was only a speed-up of an inexorable advance. Again the inroads which tiles made during the slate shortage of the early 1900s, had their beginnings in the high prices of the 1870's. Also, as far as industrial and agricultural buildings were concerned the laborious laying of slate or tiles was by the turn of the century, giving way to galvanised sheet and similar materials. Even roofs of some quarry buildings were sheeted.

The Penrhyn stoppage has been blamed for the almost total absence of outside investment in the years which followed, but in fact capital inflow had already almost vanished. In 1866, Prospectuses totalling almost a million pounds were issued, much of which was taken up. Apart from some flurries, particularly during the mid 70s, offerings steadily tapered off until in 1899 there was just one £8000 new company floated.

But there had been a more insidious factor, lack of modernisation. The slate industry entered the 20thC with a methodology established in the first half of the 19thC. Obviously this was in part due to the dearth of new money coming in, but chiefly because of the 'boom or bust' nature of the industry. In good times with profits rolling in, there seemed no need to invest, and in bad times with mounting losses, there were no resources to do so. Plus, the industry generally was reluctant to accept new ideas.

For instance, pneumatic drills which owners such as the Darbishires of Pen yr Orsedd had proved successful in the late 1880s, were still rare a decade later. It was alleged that power drilling produced cracks in the drill-holes into which powder penetrated causing a shattering of the rock. Mechanical drills did indeed produce more waste, which increased the cost of rubbish clearing, but this was a small penalty against it being fifty times Even taking full account of equipment costs, power drills more than halved the price per foot of shot-hole drilling, which was a major part of extraction costs. Even the men who would be relieved of the dreadful toil of the Jwmpah opposed powered drills. Penrhyn did not adopt them until 1912 and Dinorwig did not use them until 1919, even in the 1930s, some managers were still expressing reservations about them.

Again, in order to make a start at the foot of a working face, where no suitable natural joints were manifest, compressed-air channelling machines were available to quickly cut a 'free end' yet they were not taken up even where compressed air was available. As late as 1923, Captain (later Colonel) Martyn I. Williams-Ellis grandson of J.W. Greaves, who joined Llechwedd in 1919 stated '*The majority of quarries are still continuing to waste rock by blasting for footings*'.

American and other slate quarries had by the beginning of the 20thC., demonstrated the effectiveness of Wiresaws which in certain applications can virtually eliminate extraction waste. Moreoever since blocks so produced have at least one sawn end, mill saw-time can be reduced. Yet, apart from some experiments at Oakeley in the 1930s, they were not used in Wales until the 1980s (at Maenofferen, Llechwedd and Aberllefenni)[1].

Mill sawing was the outstanding example of outdatedness. Diamond saws were available in the 1900s yet well into the 20thC. some quarries were still using sandsaws, the rest still had Greaves pattern machines devised in the 1850s, the sole later upgrade being the occasional substitution of Hard-metal tipped blades.

The case for diamond saws was overwhelming, even the earliest machines had a feed rate of up to 12″ per minute, at least 4 times that of the traditional saw (modern machines are much faster again, 30ipm being now typical). This obviously dramatically speeded work, but even more appealing was their ability to move the blade, (or the block) sideways to position the cut, obviating the slow and laborious task of exactly locating the block on the table which traditional saws involved. It also enabled both ends of a block to be sawn without intervening manhandling. Diamond sawing also gives rise to lower feed forces, thus blocks do not normally need the careful wedging called for on the old machines. A further advantage is a better finish, so that the sawn edges of slabs often do not need further finishing. Diamond blades can be much larger than steel ones, permitting deeper cuts. They also cut many thousands of feet without attention, as against the tens of feet of a steel blade. Thus they obviate the almost daily chore of blade changing and re-sharpening, which was a particular burden on a quarry too small to have a proper saw-fettling department. Also avoided is the problem of progressive reduction of diameter (usually 24″ when new) with each re-sharpening, reducing capacity and impairing efficiency by diminishing peripheral speed.

One of the first users was Moelfferna who realising their error in equipping with sandsaws, installed an Anderson Grice machine in 1923. The daunting outlay on blades, was overcome by renting the blades on the basis of the number of feet cut, a practice that afterwards became quite usual. This saw had (and smaller modern ones usually still have) the blade on a travelling bridge, the block remaining stationary, the blade being advanced by hand. This method is still used on some machines but modern practice is to have a separate feed motor automatically controlled by the amperage demand of the blade motor.

Diamond saws were such an improvement that contemporary advice on their installation warned that the output would be so much greater than the 15 Cwt or so per day of steel saws, that the entire handling arrangements of the mill would have to be revised to cope. Such high outputs with saw speeds of 1500 rpm called for many times the approximately ½-1 hp needed by the old tables. This obviously required electric drive and lack of, (or restricted) power supplies partly accounted for their slow adoption. For in spite of the pioneering work done by a few quarries, most were laggardly in installing electricity.

Dorothea might have been the first electrified quarry, as in 1896 a costing exercise fully justified the £16,000 estimate for a hydro-plant. It was only legal problems over water rights which forced the scheme's abandonment. In view of this innovative outlook, it is odd that ten years later they should install an archaic 'Cornish' steam pump to de-water their 550′ deep pit.

Llechwedd experimented with on-site generation in 1891, putting in a full-scale 500 kw hydro plant in 1904. This showed immediate economies over clumsy, high maintenance water wheels for mill driving and incline power. For pumping, electricity obviated the use of the curious pumping-cum-haulage water-wheel remotely sited at Owain Goch (SH704473). Unusually, they also used electricity for drilling.

When the innovative Moses Kellow, having consolidated his position as manager of Parc by marrying the owner's daughter, re-opened Croesor in 1895 after a 17 year closure, he also experimented with electricity. His 350 kw 500 v hydro installation of 1904 was very much 'State of the Art' being 3 phase A.C. For mill drive and winches 10 hp motors were used, there was a 30 hp. loco and 90 hp. winder. D.C. excitation was provided by a dynamo which also lit the mill, part of the workings and Kellow's house[2].

The first public supply was from the Yale company's 589 mw Dolwen hydro plant of 1899. Votty & Bowydd used it, enabling them to abandon their steam engines, but it was to be 30 years before an augmented supply enabled them to use diamond saws. Supply on a wider scale was offered in 1905 by the North Wales Power Company's 6 mw Cwm Dyli power station. Pen yr Orsedd immediately took advantage of it, followed by Oakeley and Dinorwig and a few years later, Maenofferen[3]. The latter, in 1930, augmented this source with its own hydro plant. Its 24″ Turbo-impulse wheel was rated at 345 hp. Water at 915 cu/ft per min. on a 250′ head, turning it at 550 rpm producing 257 kw at 510/580 v. Like the Llechwedd installation, it is still in use.

But these quarries were in the minority. Penrhyn did not have a supply until 1912, and was not fully electrified until 1938, (by which time it had its own 330kw hydro plant as well as taking something like 1.5 mw from the public supply). Gradually over the years a few others including Bryneglwys (which also supplied Abergynolwyn village), put in hydro units, and others put in Diesel generators, but it was a slow process. Dorothea in spite of their early electrification plans, only finally put in a Diesel unit in the 1930s. Some such as Llwyngwern, Moelfferna and Penarth powered their generators with producer Gas engines, which were very tricky bits of kit. In 1928 Capt. Matthews of Manod quarry complained of '*The hours lost each day as men struggle to start the gas engine*'. Even in 1930 at Blaenau; Cwt y Bugail, Graig Ddu, Rhosydd and Wrysgan were all without electric power, in spite of the proximity of the new Maentwrog hydro station. It was not until the 1950s extension of Grid supplies that electric power in the quarries became universal.

In spite of the fact that at least ten times as much rubbish as good block had to be shifted, improvements in handling were almost entirely confined to block. For instance, when Cambrian were efficiently taking their block out via their tunnel, they were still laboriously uphauling most of their waste.

Such things as water-balances were clung to, even in quarries with an electric supply, in the belief that they were 'free', yet it was shown that the slowness, high maintenence and labour intensiveness of such devices made them far more costly to run than electric haulages. In 1938 Votty and Bowydd were still using a water balance which the Quarry Manager's Journal described as '*70 years old, lifting only one truck at a time and taking five minutes to do so. Men at the top and the bottom are required to operate the valves, as the automatic stops have not worked for many years*'.

156

Again, many Welsh quarries had been in the forefront in the adoption of steam locos, but they were retained long after electric traction had been shown to be more economical, (and could be run on lighter track). It was understandable that due to the problems of overhead wires, particularly underground, Moses Kellow's initiative in using electric locos was not widely copied. But even when suitable accumulators became available, battery-electric traction was not very widely taken up. Such units were more expensive to buy and run than wire-fed electric locos but were proven cheaper than steam and certainly more economical than the horses which were still widely employed. Admittedly a horse and driver's costs were half those of a battery loco[4], but could only do a fifth as much work. Llechwedd at least, would eventually use electric traction with, by the early 1930s, all their underground locos battery and their surface locos overhead-wire (the latter being mostly in-house conversions of old steam locos). At that time it was claimed that the running costs of battery locos were 30% less, and conductor types 40% less, than steam units. Even when cheap and versatile internal-combustion locos became available, old, and often worn-out steam locos were retained at most quarries.

Anyway, up to date or not, in the early 1900s quarries vied to make up the shortfall caused by the Penrhyn stoppage which had abruptly cut Welsh output by almost 20%. In spite of some slackness in the building trade, it was all go, with by 1903, the best slate fetching more than the peak prices of 1876.

In 1904, in Nantlle, Moel Tryfan had almost 300 men[5], and had put in 7 new saws to bring their total to 44. Braich Rhyd had 58 men and were putting in a new drainage tunnel. Fron had 39 men, with 8 saws in the mill (they had taken on 50 men when they re-opened in 1901, but this included men on development) and Braich had 80 men and 13 saw tables. Of the big quarries only Cilgwyn and Alexandra, each with 200 men at work were below their best ever. In spite of the general briskness, some of the smaller workings fared less well. Brynfferam, for instance, after stumbling on with a handful of men, had folded in 1902.

At Llanberis, Cefn Du had around 125 men at work, (including

20 at Bwlch y Groes), and Cook & Ddôl had 25 men and had installed 7 new saws. In Cwm Gwyrfai, Hafod y Wern employed 36. In the Bethesda area at Moel Faban, Afon Wen and Cwm Bychan, 16 men, 8 men and 2 men respectively found employment which was denied them at Penrhyn. Elsewhere some very small workings were revived, such as the ancient Tal y Fan near Conwy where 7 men were employed. In Caernarfonshire as a whole, times were undoubtedly good, although not as good as a County Council publicity leaflet put out at this time claimed. Its claim that there were 99 slate quarries in the county was a considerable overstatement, as many abandoned sites were listed.

In the Blaenau area 18 quarries were working, with even the smallest doing well. Llechwedd had a record payroll of well over 600, Bwlch y Slaters had 52 men and were talking of expansion, considering putting in electricity, even planning to light the chambers. The somewhat marginal Pantmawr had their 20 men making fresh underground developments. Blaen y Cwm had 12 men, and were making new works, as were Graig Ddu and Cwt y Bugail. Little Foelgron had 8 men, Drum 4 and Croes y Ddwy Afon had a surprising 62.

Further south such scratchings as Rhaeadr got in on the act, and near Dinbych, Aber's 3 men and Nantglyn's 4 were busy hand-working their slab products, taking advantage of the larger quarries preoccupation with roofing slate. There were also several openings or re-openings such as Aberdunant and Cwm Teigl, mostly with just one or two water-powered saws and perhaps half a dozen men.

Unfortunately this euphoria was short lived, for apart from the extra tonnage as Penrhyn's production built up, the building industry took a further downturn. Blaenau suffered an additional setback when their main export outlet, Germany, imposed a 30% import duty on slate. By 1904 with imports booming, the market went into surplus, bringing to a stop the shortage-driven price rises. The 1905 lists came out 5-7% down, and there was an unprecedented further mid-year price cut, a step which had not been necessary even in the tough times of the late 1870s. Wages were reduced by around 5% and men were laid off or put on short time. There was a wave of strikes particularly in the Nantlle area, which were not entirely unwelcome to owners carrying heavy stocks and hard put to meet wage bills.

A continuing fall in demand drove tonnages for 1906 almost 25% below those of a couple of years before, with prices slashed by a similar percentage. There were further cuts in manning, particularly in Nantlle. Although Cilgwyn held up well with 217 men and Fron was up to 44, Alexandra was down to 190 and Moel Tryfan to 243, many of whom were on short time. Others such as Nant y Fron only recently a 100 man operation, slid into closure. Elsewhere several smaller quarries such as Croes y Ddwy Afon, Foelgron and Henddol closed. The recently revived Aberdunant succumbed but Cwm Teigl's 3 men still hung on, and down at Arthog another 3 kept going at this recently re-opened site. Against the trend just a few were able to take men on. Hafod y Wern increased their payroll to 51 and Moel Faban to 44, for them a big number.

The tiny diggings that jobless Penrhyn men had started in all sorts of unlikely and out of the way places northward from Bethesda almost to the coast, folded. Some had found rock which could be reduced and carried back many miles at the end of the day to be sold for a few pennies to help feed a family. Some had found nothing, scarcely any repaid the labour of tunneling and the erection of crude shelters.

It was becoming clear that the 1901-1904 mini-boom had been just a respite from an inexorable shrinkage. The industry was in trouble, deep trouble and no part of it more than the slab trade. Some folk might still want slate on their roofs but not on their floors. The fashion was for mantelpieces of timber not slate, concrete lintels, windowsills and doorsteps were coming into widespread use. Galvanised tanks and cement rendering were displacing slate on the farms. Gentlemen now relieved themselves against Messrs. Shanks' wares, and the gruesome slate privy seat was now just a chilly memory. Even in the graveyards, the more pretentious tended to be memorialized in alien stone. The tables on which the supposedly dissolute Edwardian youths cued their billiards balls were more likely to have Italian beds than Welsh. Penrhyn did retain some trade with Germany in billiards table slab, but it is said that in fact these were required for fabricating vats for the production of munitions! The newfangled electric installations did call for slate switchboards, but their requirements were as yet modest. The problems of the slab-dependant quarries were compounded by the mixed-product units turning to slab to stem their falling outputs. Braich Goch fell victim in 1906, gutting the village of Corris. A classic example of a quarry folding because profits earned in the good years had been dispersed. This had left it unable to undertake development work which could have made it less dependant on slab.

Export prospects were far from good. More overseas countries, particularly where indigenous slate industries were being nurtured, imposed tariffs, which where these did not actually close a market, forced prices down. Vainly men showed their protest, particularly again in Nantlle by a number of strikes. From 1907 to 1909 sales sagged further, listed prices did edge up, but whether actual prices obtained increased is questionable, particularly as import prices were coming down. A London merchant who had paid £7 5 0 (£7.25) for a mille of French slate in 1906, claimed he could, by 1909 obtain the same grade and size for £5 2 6 (£5.125). As always, there were little diggings which somehow, for a time at least, bucked the trend. The abandoned and isolated Powys quarry revived and nearby Cwmmaengwynedd found work for 20 men, about five times their usual number, but these were ephemeral exceptions.

1910 and 1911 were better years, with some slight recovery in sales and some firming of prices. But Tan-y-Bwlch and Moel Faban co-operative once a 270 man operation, failed, although their third quarry, Pantdreiniog did continue under different ownership until 1926. All the several attempts at worker ownership proved fragile. Co-operative working at Llyn y Gader was no more successful than had been the previous attempt there, by the NWQMU in 1881, and the Cook and Ddôl co-op fared little better.

In 1912 tonnages dropped again. Bad debt increased, with even some reputable merchants failing, owing substantial sums to quarry firms. In 1912 Pen yr Orsedd lost £582 and Tal y Sarn £82 when Smith of Nottingham went through, and that summer several other Nantlle quarries reported bad trade and credit problems. In fact most in the Nantlle area were finding times hard, Gloddfa'r Coed which had once employed 150 men were now down to 7. Those on Crown leases were seeking abatement of dues. It being pointed out that a quarry lease was typically at 30/ (£1.50) per acre, whereas similar land was let for agriculture at only £1. Plus Crown royalties ran at 2/ — 2/6 (10p — 12.5p) against the 1/6 — 1.10 (7.5p — 9p) charged by many private landowners. It was claimed that anything up to 40 tons or more of debris had to be shifted for every ton of slate made. At 9d (3.75p) per ton this could add up to almost half the average selling price of £3 10 0 (£3.50) per ton. In addition, several Nantlle quarries were spending 2/- (10p) on pumping for each ton of slate made, and one was said to be spending 5/- (25p) per ton.

For 1913, prices were boldly jacked up to levels close to the 1903-04 boom, which did help margins a little, but helped imports a lot, which for the first time exceeded exports. An untimely strike in the building trade pushed Welsh production down to 300,000 tons, and manning to 9000, a drop of nearly 40% in little more than a decade. Tan yr Allt closed making some 70 men idle, nearby Fron was fading fast. Bwlch Cwmllan which had over the past ten years managed to keep around 20 men in work, succumbed to their transport problems. Rhiwbach failed, as did the following year, the very efficient Parc & Croesor company, and in Meirionnydd generally many found trade difficult.

One tiny section of the industry that did seem to hold its own were the little quarries producing whetstones. These Hones besides being used by woodworkers for their edge tools, also replaced the traditional wooden rips which, coated with grease and sand, were used to sharpen scythes and sickles. Handfuls of men survived, making 2 or 3 tons or so apiece per year at tiny, remote sites. All that was required was a source of close-grained rock and a stream to power a sand-saw (and also possibly a polishing machine). With such a small weight of product no elaborate transport was needed. Thus with a tonnage value of perhaps £30, these little ventures could be relatively profitable. Although Melynllyn, for instance, closed in 1908, production was transferred to and expanded at Moel Siabod, which survived until almost 1920, when it was squeezed out by the same pressures of factory made product and foreign competition as beset the slate industry proper.

With the 1913 price increases seen as counter productive, prices for 1914 were cut by 5%, with inevitably, a reduction in wages exacerbating the problems caused by layoffs and giving rise to disputes such as the 4 month strike by the 220 men at Alexandra. This Alexandra strike heralded a new direction in industrial relations, as it was an official Union call-out. The strikes around 1905-06, with the NWQMU in disarray, had been backed by the chapels rather than the Union. The more serious confrontations of earlier years, although union supported, had not been initiated by the union. This change was due to the energetic leadership of R.T. Jones who, having greatly increased the Union's membership, had taken matters out of the hands of the quarry lodges and placed them firmly in the central committee's control. Within a few years Jones would achieve almost 100% membership, enabling the NWQMU to speak with one voice on behalf of all the workers in the industry.

The old order was also changing on the management side. Besides there being a new Lord Penrhyn, E.A. Young died in 1910. Two years later W.E. Oakeley, little more than an onlooker since his quarries had been in the hands of a limited company dominated by Hoare's Bank, also passed on. New men were emerging, owing their position to ability and energy rather than descent or privilege. They would bring new ideas and a new ethos, not only the industry but also to society in general. Like their predecessors they would hold office as Councillors, Magistrates,

High Sheriffs and Lords Lieutenant, but unlike them, as servants of their communities rather than as masters.

But of course, far greater changes were at hand. In early 1914 trade remained slack, but by mid year there seemed grounds for sober optimism. The long dry Summer did pose problems of water shortage, but the shooting of a foreign princeling in an obscure Balkan town, cannot have caused great anxiety in the cabans, the taverns or even the boardrooms of Bethesda and Blaenau.

[1] Early Wire Saws, consisted of an indented endless wire typically 3/16″ thick, cutting the rock by being fed with sand and water. These wires might be several hundred yards long, led over pulleys to a distant steam engine. Modern ones are self-contained units with integral compressed air motors, cutting by diamond-impregnated collars threaded onto the wire).

[2] Moses Kellow also developed (and manufactured on site) a patent hydraulic drill. He invented a hydraulic channelling machine and developed an innovative high pressure pump. His many inventions included hydraulic motors and various dewatering equipment. He made improvements in sawing and in underground working methods. Whilst not all his devices were completely successful, he was arguably the most ingenious engineer the slate industry ever had.

[3] At first publicly supplied electricity cost 1d per KWH equivalent to .313p per hp per hour. This represented a coal equivalent of £2.80 per ton, (2½lb/hp/hr.), over double the average the cost of coal. However the far greater efficiency of electricity, the fact that it was only used as needed instead of a boiler continuously in steam (and required no fireman and little maintenance), outweighed the apparent higher cost. When after WW1 the price of electicity halved and that of coal almost doubled, the case for electrification became overwhelming.

[4] A 1912 reckoning showed a horse as costing 17/6 (87.5p) to feed, plus 2/3 (11.5p) for depreciation, and £1 drivers wages. A battery loco's total costs were a little over £4.

[5] In 1904 Moel Tryfan had 105 Bargainers, 52 Rubbishers, 34 Badrockmen, 44 Untoppers, 3 Weighers and 39 on various duties. Daily wages averaged from a little over 5/- (25p) for the Bargainers to not much more than half that for the Rubbishers.

11. Dogged Struggles
1914-1939

The outbreak of war in August 1914, put the slate trade into confusion. Commercial confidence ebbed, the building industry wound down, orders were cancelled and exports (and imports) vanished. All shipping movements were strictly controlled, quarry steamers were commandeered for war service, some such as the Penrhyn vessel Linda Blanche soon to be torpedoed. Rail carriage was uncertain, civilian consignments often being left in sidings to clear the tracks for troop trains and 'Jellicoe Specials' carrying coal for the Fleet. Several quarries closed and most others went to short-time working. A number had their financial problems exacerbated by large sums outstanding from German customers.

However by 1916 in spite of the ban on building, it was not the shortage of orders or the problems of transport which was constricting output, but the shortage of men. A great many had volunteered for the forces, others had taken jobs in war factories, a number of which had been set up in or near the quarries, taking advantage of the industry's equipment and technical expertise. One such factory, for making shells, was at the FR.'s Boston Lodge works. Llechwedd's steam haulage engine was requisitioned to power it, an electric motor being installed as a replacement.

In 1917 the slate industry was classed as non-essential and many of its remaining men were conscripted or directed into work of 'National Importance'. The standard pay for the latter being £2 12 6 (£2.62) per week, plus 17/6 (87.2p) lodging allowance. This was widely considered derisory, but to slate workers it must have seemed handsome. A few quarries broke with tradition by employing women in their offices. Occasionally, women such as Miss Kane who ran Pen yr Orsedd in the 1850s, have been involved in management, women also once helped their menfolk carry slates from tiny early diggings, and in early times girls sometimes drove pannier-ponies. This apart, female employment was unknown.

Some quarries barred women underground even as visitors, in the belief that a death would ensue.

Additionally, the non-essential classification, put the quarries at the back of the queue for coal and other vital supplies. Blaenau output dropped to 20,000 tons, less than a quarter of the immediate prewar total, with fewer than 900 men at work. Llechwedd had 110 men compared with a peak of over 600. Other areas were slightly less badly hit, but the 1917 industry total of under 100,000 tons and 3000 men scarcely exceeded the prewar figures of Dinorwig alone.

Quarries increasingly were having to turn business away, and merchants' yards and quarry banks were bare of even the most unsaleable varieties. War-time paper shortages meant that even writing slates were being asked for. With only 10 quarries of any size still open, demand greatly exceeded supply. In January 1918 The Slate Trade Gazette reported '*We are informed that for some time the demand for slate has been double the output and that, as a consequence, there is likely to be a slate famine within a few months. The difficulty is, and will continue to be, the provision of adequate labour*'.

Prices which had only risen by 5% since 1914, were sharply increased, followed by unprecedented quarterly revisions, which by October brought them to almost 50% above the record levels of 1903/04.

The war's end in November 1918 brought an immediate surge of orders for the back-log of new building and of repairs. Foreign suppliers being busy with their own problems, buyers almost stormed the gates of U.K. quarries. Price lists issued at the beginning of 1919 showed only modest advances, but by mid 1920, six-monthly jumps took levels to almost double those of late 1918. The Slate Trade Gazette reporting in May 1920, (just prior to a further price hike), that '*Best Portmadoc Blues which sold for £11 13 0 (£11.65) in 1914, fetched £27 10 0 (£27.50) last July, are now fetching £35*'.

Most of the quarries such as Bryneglwys and Diffwys which had closed during the war re-opened. A new company took on Rhiwbach, one of their first actions being to raise the charges on their tramroad, to the detriment of quarries using it. Maenofferen solved the problem temporarily by running out through Votty & Bowydd and in 1928, permanently, by buying out Rhiwbach. Bwlch y Slaters ceased to use it, dispatching via the Cwm Teigl road. Amalgamated Slate was formed to re-open Cilgwyn and some neighbouring quarries, and soon employed over 400 men. Several of the small Nantlle workings were revived, and elsewhere even doubtful sites such as Nantyr in Glyn Ceiriog, had a new lease of life.

As regards capital, some new money was coming in, sometimes from unexpected sources, such as the 1920 purchase of Croes y Ddwy Afon and the following year of Rhosydd, by Colmans (of mustard fame). Several companies were formed, such as a £20,000 flotation to re-open Fronlog and the £35,000 company at Cwm Machno. In south Wales there was a £40,000 scheme at Glogue, to erect a 100' x 38' mill with 4 saws and 2 planers all water-turbine powered, as well as a plant to make bricks from waste. There were some obvious non-starters such as the £300,000, Welsh Slate Combine, intended to take in Cwt y Bugail and Braich Goch. (These quarries were subsequently successfully separately floated.) But, in spite of the boom, capitalists generally stayed away.

Also staying away were the men. Many quarrymen had found in the forces, better food and better clothing than they had previously known. They had discovered that what the Army called a barracks was very different from say, the Rhosydd connotation of the term. After the wages paid in munition factories, even the enhanced rewards now being offered in slate quarrying seemed paltry. Plus, there were those who could never come back, as memorials in quarrying districts testify, these were sadly numerous[1].

Apart from the shortage of men, particularly skilled men, there was a shortage of plant. New equipment was expensive and on extended delivery, and high prices were asked for such second hand items that had escaped being melted down for armaments. There were however plenty of War Department locos coming onto the market. Most were steam, many American built, intended for use on the narrow gauge tracks laid down to supply the army's trenches and depots. Thus there were opportunities to modernise rail motive power at least. Some of these locos were diesel or petrol engined units, giving some quarries their first introduction to this more economical form of traction. (Capt. T.P. Crossland's decision to replace his steam loco by a Simplex petrol unit in the long tunnel at Cambrian quarry was based on his seeing them at work in France during the war, so successful was this that a similar Planet loco was bought in 1929.)

More significant in the longer term, was the great number of motor lorries the Government was releasing. Moel y Faen and Clogau had already abandoned the Oernant tramway, product being taken to Llangollen station by steam lorry. The availability of motor lorries encouraged other quarries to consider road haulage. Indeed slate could now be economically worked entirely independent of rail connection. Cwm Bach near Tremadog, one of the very few entirely new openings in the 1920s, was totally road haulage dependent.

Some slate shipments resumed, but not only were exports little more than token, but also the post-war shortage of vessels made coast-wise shipping expensive. Even after sea-freight rates collapsed, a reduction in railway rates would ensure that most U.K. distribution would be by rail. Caernarfon even handled an unprecedented slate import! (Italian slab for a manufacturing merchant in the town), and within a few years the port would be described as *'Deserted and grass-grown, with even harbour buildings being re-roofed in asbestos sheet'*.

With a fierce demand, the industry did the best it could and in 1920 neared 200,000 tons, a creditable recovery, but still only two-thirds of the worst of the immediate prewar years. Coal continued to be scarce and dear, serious shortages arising during the 1921 coal strike. Thus water power regained some of its old importance, but for several weeks, in the dry summer of 1921, up to 2000 men were idle, due to water shortage. Conversely, Dorothea would soon have too much water, for in 1922 there was a recurrence of the flooding problem, which had been disastrous in

1884 and had caused a stoppage in 1910. There were no casualties but almost 200,000 tons of ground collapsed into the pit carrying away a Blondin and two public roads. (12 years later the mess was still not fully cleared.)

There were also industrial relations problems looming. In 1918 when even agricultural labourers were doing better than quarrymen, a minimum wage had been established and at least the outline of a sliding scale, tying wages to slate prices. By 1921 comparatively generous concessions on wages and hours had been recommended by the two employers' associations, who represented the larger owners[2]. The more affluent quarries could afford to pay these sort of rates, the smaller ones could not. Their men felt aggrieved, and their wives, faced with escalating prices in the shops, even more so.

In 1921, in spite of the problems, production was up again, tonnages well exceeding 200,000, with pundits predicting *'Ten to fifteen years of prosperity'*. But users faced with shortages and high prices, were already turning to other sources and other products. Reports began to appear that certain sizes were in poor demand, then towards the end of the year, amongst a flood of order cancellations, the queue for deliveries vanished.

It was clear that prices for 1922 would have to be slashed with wage rates reduced in accordance with the sliding scale. But, when the 1922 lists were published they had not gone down by the expected 18%, on which the wage reduction had been based, but only by 10%. Though this cut was less than the dramatic fall in living costs which occurred during late 1921, the men, understandably, felt they had been cheated out of almost 1/ (5p) per day. Furthermore, the owners thought the minimum wage was too high and they pressed to reduce it by a third. Whilst few employers would oppose the concept of a 'living wage', there was the fear that if a minimum was too close to what a poorish Bargain would pay, the team might be tempted to produce little or nothing.

In March there was trouble and by June almost the whole of the was on strike. Though a few quarries stayed idle for up to four months, most men were back in two weeks, substantially on managements terms. Throughout the industry the settlement gave little satisfaction to either side, as managements were commited to wage rates tied to list prices which were often much above levels at which sales could actually be made. The men, certainly those on short time, were still taking home poor wages.

At the end of the year, with heavy stocks particularly in the smaller sizes, the 1923 lists came out a further 10% down, triggering a corresponding fall in wages. Over a couple of years average earnings fell by a third and the minimum wage was down from 12/6 (62.5p) per day to 6/6 (32.5p).

Many of the industry's problems were beginning to look fundamental. For instance, increasingly house building was by national firms and by direct-labour municipal authorities. These big buyers demanded vast numbers of identical items, to a close specification, with tight delivery dates and possibly non-performance penalties. Few slate quarries could meet such terms, but almost any tile maker could. The continental quarries were fast recovering from the war, and although imports were well below the immediate prewar totals, they were growing apace and in 1921 exceeded 6500 tons, with France again the main source but with Portugal taking an increasing share. Exports were a mere 3-4000 tons. The 120,000 tons which Germany had once taken had vanished and Australia once an 8000 ton market was now a trickle. A press report of the time pointed out that in *recent years the slate industry had shown no growth, but the tile industry is now three times what it had been*.

During 1923, difficulties continued, whilst few men were wholly unemployed, many were on short time, with Saturday working the exception. Total output fell to 160,000 tons, over 20% down on the 1921 peak, with the Caernarfonshire quarries being particularly badly hit, some such as Pen yr Orsedd temporarily closing. In the north-east, Deeside, tied to the declining slab market and with ageing machinery, closed.

Blaenau's position remained relatively strong. Wrysgan, which had re-opened in 1922 after nearly 20 years idleness, was under new ownership and putting in new plant. Oakeley re-opened Nyth y Gigfran, by tunnelling in from its own upper workings, so eliminating the earlier vertiginous operations on narrow ledges, and Bwlch y Slaters expanded, taking in the adjacent Old Manod site. Cwt y Bugail would shortly flourish under new ownership and in south Wales, Glogue, its one remaining quarry of any consequence, installed 4 additional saws.

Also against the general trend, some small workings were revived, such as Hendre Ddu (Dinas Mawddwy) and Natyr, which the curiously named 'Square Slate Quarries Ltd' took over from the defunct National Welsh Company. In Cwm Gwyrfai, there was a flurry of activity. Hafod y Wern re-opened albeit briefly, as the Victoria quarry, after a decade of near idleness. Rhos Clogwyn, re-started on a modest scale, abandoned their incline, reaching the NWNGR by a ropeway. A buyer was found for Treflan and Llyn y Gadair was revived. Several quarries, such as Bryn Hafod y Wern, were now being worked on a small scale by men unable to find other employment, sharing profits, if any, between them. This 'Free enterprise', incidentally, did not appeal to the Union (now amalgamated with the T. & G.W.U.) which demanded in 1923 that if a quarry could not pay men at least £2 per week, it should be closed.

There was some improvement in trade in 1924 but financial returns remained poor. Goverment help was sought, particularly in the matter of the use of slate for official buildings. Representations were again made to help quarries on Crown land by the abatement of royalties, and assistance was sought to combat imports.

There was talk of strengthening 'Brand Images' but an attempt by Votty & Bowydd to do this, failed partly due to the problems of marking the product. An industry-wide publicity campaign to promote the use of slate was mooted but it was thought that the merchanting system made this too difficult. Merchants were coming in for a lot of stick at this time, it was alleged that they were increasing their mark-ups to compensate for lower prices, it being said that instead of the traditional 10-15% they were now getting 15-20%. Some were said to be regarding the extra 60 they got in every Mille, not as an allowance for breakages, but as part of the count and making claims for any mille that was not of 1260 saleable pieces. It was also said that they were lax in emphasising to buyers that the Welsh mille meant 1200, whereas import prices were based on the bare 1000. In fact the whole question of count was confused. Most quarries sold by the mille, although a few such as Croesor sold by the actual 1000, as did most London merchants. Elsewhere the mille still ruled and at least one court case arose through a dispute over how many was a 'thousand'.

There was also disquiet at the varying names given by various quarries to differing qualities, buyers were confused by such terms as 'Best', 'First', 'Strong Deep' and so on. The number of varieties offered was criticised. (Penrhyn was listing nearly 250 different items.)

Credit, always the bane of the industry, stretched to 3 or 4 months, and there were bad debt problems. The traditional method of solving 'cash flow' difficulties by holding back wages (which were by now generally weekly) being no longer an option. With money tight, big stocks of unpopular sizes both at the quarries and in merchants yards on consignment terms (i.e. paid for when sold), were an embarrassment. There was still a tendency to always seek to make the biggest and best slates that could be made out of a particular block, even when perhaps smaller and cheaper slates were in better demand. Critics pointed out that it was better to make a product which could be sold rather than a nominally slightly more profitable one which had to be put down as stock.

By 1925 trade was picking up and short time working became the exception and there were reopenings at Henddol, Llanfair, Westminster, Foelgron, Moelfre (after a 40 year closure), and a brief re-opening of Tal y Sarn. New companies were formed at Llangynog and Graig Ddu, the latter putting in a new oil-engined compressor to work drills, a winch and a pump. Both Croes y Ddwy Afon, and Rhiwbach put in new saws and compressors, but when Chwarel Ddu, revived as Castle quarry, ordered a solitary

10hp pump such expenditure was considered sufficiently newsworthy to be reported in the trade press.

Outputs improved further in 1926, in spite of the coal strike causing some hold ups, and in 1927 the quarter million tons was exceeded for the first time since the war. But the growing pressure of imports which had leapt to almost 50,000 tons, kept prices weak at about 17½% below the 1921 peak.

In 1928 trade was slack, by 1929 it was definitely poor. Some optimism remained in what was left of the slab trade, with tiny Craig y Cribin re-opening after many years idleness, but Hafod Las' closure was more typical of its continuing decline. This was reflected in contractions in the independent manufacturing trade. Williams Eureka at Port Dinorwig had been taken over by Dixons of Bangor and in 1924 they amalgamated with Fletchers of Victoria Dock, Caernarfon. As Fletcher-Dixon they maintained their ability to make large fabrications, such as a tank produced in 1930 reputedly 24' long, 9' wide, 11'6" high made of 38 slabs of Penrhyn slate 2½" thick, weighing 28 tons, but their billiards tables and enamelled products had dwindled to almost nothing.

A more than 10% reduction in the 1930 price lists failed to stem a steepening dive into recession. At first Dinorwig managed to keep their 2000 men on full time, partly because they had captured much of Nantlle's Irish trade. Thus Nantlle which had already lost nine quarries since 1914 (Blaen y Cae, Braich, Cloddfa'r Coed, Cloddfa'r Lon, Gloddfa Glai, Gwernor, Tal y Sarn, Tan yr Allt & Tŷ Mawr) was further hit, with Fronheulog, Pen yr Orsedd, Dorothea and Pen y Bryn all laying men off in the new year. Nantlle was also choking on its own debris. There being limits to how high it could be piled and how many disused pits could be filled. There was a revival of the old idea of a collective rubbish railway to the sea, but finding finance for such a big project was out of the question.

By March 1930, depression was spreading. Many more quarries announced short-time working, even Dinorwig having to go onto a 3 day week. Some such as Glynrhonwy and the comparatively buoyant Bryneglwys suspended work completely. In June, 600

Welsh slatemen were reported as unemployed and 2000 as being on short time. By the end of the year, little more than 200,000 tons had been sold and many of the men who had been on short time were now totally without work. There were shock failures such as that of the Llanberis Slate Company which had been operating Cefn Ddu and Chwarel Fawr. Happily import tonnages were also down, partly due to a new requirement to mark them 'Foreign', but they still topped 40,000 tons.

In 1931, in spite of prices being trimmed a further 5% there was no respite. At the start of the year the total of slate quarry workers reported at various Labour Exchanges as unemployed or on short time were: Bethesda 1456, Llanberis 1322, Penygroes (Nantlle valley) 532, Bangor 58, Blaenau Ffestiniog 86, Porthmadog 83, Pwllheli 2. By June 1931, the Union reported that for the industry as a whole, only 700 men were working a full 5½ day week, 1000 were on 5 days, 2750 were on 4 days, 2100 were averaging 2½ days and 130 were unemployed. Such figures suggest that employers were trying to avoid total lay-offs, though hard economics might have favoured total temporary closure. In Nantlle there were further body blows. Both Pen y Bryn and Old Pen y Bryn failed, likewise Amalgamated Slate, making 500 men jobless at Cilgwyn, Moel Tryfan and Alexandra, the latter still suffering the effects of the 1927 gale which blew down the Blondin masts. In 1922 there had been 11 firms operating in the Nantlle area, employing nearly 1700 men. By the end of 1931 there were just 4 employing 865. Invariably when a company went through, the men were left not only idle but with wage arrears unpaid. Such closures also had a 'knock on' effect on the quarries' suppliers, they having to cut staffing and suffer bad debts.

The hard times again fell most heavily on north Caernarfonshire. This was reflected in house prices. In Bethesda, £30 was an average price for small properties, some two bedroomed cottages sold for £15 and quite substantial 3 bedroomed dwellings only fetched £60. The Blaenau area fared better, Oakeley and others had periods of short time working, but these were mostly brief. Of the only 8 quarries in Wales having more than 100 men in full-time employment, 4 were in Blaenau, (Oakeley, Llechwedd, Maenofferen, Votty & Bowydd). Blaenau's fortunes were also helped by the few vital pence more that their products could command over the likes of Penrhyn and Dinorwig. Some Nantlle prices also held up well, with Dorothea commanding a slight premium over even Blaenau.

Imports were still making heavy inroads into the market. French prices had increased but were still way under Welsh prices. In 1931 10 ton lots of 'Best Quality' Fumay French slates were being offered at Harwich quay for £23 18 6 (£23.925). At that time Best Blaenau slate would cost about £33.60 at Porthmadog and even Seconds would have been £28.30. (As part of their marketing exercise, the importers declared that French slate was *'Guaranteed not to turn white'*. It was roundly retorted that Welsh slate *'required no such guarantee'*!) Besides the price advantage, imports benefited from the configuration of the rail network which made it easier and cheaper, to reach main markets from the Channel or east coast ports than from the Welsh slate districts. As regards home-produced competitive materials, one report priced 100 sq. ft of roofing in cement tiles at £1.50 against over £3 for Welsh slate.

In late 1931 the hope that the abandonment of the Gold standard would help exports, boosted confidence. Dinorwig which had been on a 2 week month went to full time, and despairing of getting orderliness into the huge hotchpotch the workings had become, made a tentative new opening at Marchlyn. This project, like Cwm Bach, exemplifying how the motor lorry now enabled an opening to be made without any regard for rail access. Dorothea, also on a 2 week month went to a 3 week month and then to full time, and even took men on. Penrhyn also resumed full week working. At the end of 1931 although the numbers totally unemployed had not fallen, there were fewer on short time. In 1932 the Caernarfonshire Crown Quarry Co., who had been doing well at Rhos, re-opened Moel Tryfan, electrified and took on 20 men. They also acquired Cilgwyn, Braich and Alexandra, repairing the latter's mill which had been damaged by fire during the closure. They did not work Braich but attempted to make a new opening (New Crown) between it and Moel Tryfan, but its success was limited, as in fact was their whole Nantlle operation. Dorothea absorbed Gallt y Fedw and South Dorothea. They also took on and re-started Pen y Bryn, but within months had to abandon it. The small Fronlog took over Gwernor and Tŷ Mawr East to re-commence small-scale working. In Dinbych, Moelfferna installed a third diamond saw to cope with the extra business they inherited when neighbour and rival Penarth closed. By this time diamond saws had an additional attraction in that they cut heavily doused in an oil-water emulsion, often avoiding the extractors which regulations now demanded for steel saws. Besides the expense of ducting, extractor fans could well absorb almost as much power as the saws they served.

In 1932 the Welsh output managed to stay above 200,000 tons, but with exports weak Blaenau's share decreased. Also, although some quarries were moving more product, returns for all but the largest and most efficient were below break even levels. In fact in spite of the increase in the use of power of all kinds[3], the whole industry had become less efficient. In the 1880s outputs per man in open quarries in north Wales had averaged 31 tons with underground workings slightly more. By the 1930s open workings were only averaging 24 tons/man year, with underground workings even less. This was partly due to the reduction in hours and to the smaller proportion of slab product and also, it was alleged, to men *'regarding modern machinery as being to their benefit not that of the quarry'*. But worryingly, much of the fall in productivity was due to good rock becoming more difficult to win. Average make to waste ratios had been around 1-15, now 1-20 was usual, with Penrhyn reported as getting a mere 1-100 in the upper galleries. Quarries were said to be spending 15% of gross revenue on waste removal.

The struggles of 1932 and 1933 brought further wage reductions as hard pressed firms tried to balance their books. Economically, the quarries were trying to climb a downgoing escalator. Price reductions which should have made their product more competitive were being more than matched by the fall in the price of tiles. Tile production and imports though below their 1927 peaks, still aggregated to the equivalent of almost half a million tons of slate.

There were pontifications in the trade press alleging short-sightedness by owners. It was said with some truth, that quarries fought each other for business, rather than presenting a united front against the tile industry. Their bad state of repair was often criticised. An instance was made of the condition of quarry rail lines which required the continued use of old and inefficient double-flanged wheeled trucks, laboriously dragged over collapsing track. It was suggested that *'management would rather spend £10 per week keeping track repaired than pay £25 to replace it'*. Sound advice — to anyone with £25. Wrysgan was an instance of the marginal state of some quarries. Their spectacular self acting incline, failing to 'self act', had been converted to single acting, hauling empties up by a steam engine. Unfortunately the boiler was too small so journeys stalled through lack of steam. When mains electricity was put in to work the mill, it was decided to electrically haul the incline. Since a motor could not be afforded, when empty trucks needed to be raised, the mill motor was unbolted, then dragged from the mill to the incline-head where it was temporarily installed to power the incline. Eventually an old lorry engine was used, and also another incline was powered by the engine of a scrapped car. At this time stringencies were not confined to the quarries. On one occasion when a man was injured at Croesor in 1930, an ambulance was called. The vehicle's brakes proved so defective that men with ropes had to hold it back on the road down from the quarry!

In 1933 fortunes were mixed. Tonnages overall held up, with Blaenau recovering well. Hoare's put extra capital into Oakeley enabling them to buy Votty & Bowydd (and 2 years later Diffwys), and to seek new rock by re-developing Cwmorthin. The dewatering of Cwmorthin old Vein section was not a problem, but to drain 45 million gallons from 70 flooded chambers on the Back Vein, called for specialist contractors who made a 5″ borehole through from the existing workings. As a result their 800 men who had been working a 10 day month, went onto full time. Hoare's

Bank sought an amalgamation with Llechwedd but their £440,000 valuation of Oakeley and £90,000 for Llechwedd met with understandable derision from the Llechwedd board. Also Mrs Inge, daughter of W.E. Oakeley who had inherited part of her father's share in the Oakeley Quarries, was firmly advised to have nothing to do with it. Thus the bid fell though.

Llechwedd, although its 400 or so payroll was half that of Oakeley, was a much more valuable property partly due to the innovative enterprise of Martyn Williams-Ellis. He had extended the electrification, with a Diesel set to back up the hydro plant and had introduced electric traction. Always stressing the great economies that could be made, by improving waste handling, he put in an overhead conveyor for the purpose. Such ropeways were usual in Lake District quarries but his system was unique in the Welsh slate industry. This conveyor also served his pioneering untopping scheme. Mechanical excavators, or 'steam navvies' had been used by such quarries as Pen yr Orsedd and Penrhyn for rubbish removal. Williams-Ellis was one of the first to realise that with more powerful Diesel excavators available, it was practicable to strip off the overburden from old underground workings, thus exposing the pillars, which represented perhaps 40′ width of good slate rock. Oakeley had considered untopping in the 1890s but it was not actually done there until the 1980s. Several other quarries such as Blaen y Cwm untopped to a limited degree, but Llechwedd was the first to fully adopt this method, although the necessary buying out of grazing rights cost them dear. Untopping is now the basis of almost all Blaenau work. Williams-Ellis also introduced an unusual monorail system to assist with movement of finished slate from mill to stock yard, possibly copying a system which may have been used at Hafod Las. He also developed slate powder manufacture.

At Penrhyn trade was now better and they put in extra pumps as the lowest workings were now 200′ below the drainage adit. The immense task of de-watering a big pit working is shown by figures published by Major Griffith, the Penrhyn manager. These showed that each 1″ of rain meant something like 22,500 tons of water entering his quarry. In addition to surface water this deepening also meant that much of the 800 tons of water the water-balances used each day also had to be pumped, making them clearly much more costly to run than electric hoists. Although only a third of the water had to be pumped, 150 hp from water-power and 567 hp from electricity was required to do so.

Elsewhere trade was thin, Dinorwig for a time laid off 400 men, Aberllefenni operated a 3-day week and many others also cut back. Dorothea added Old Pen y Bryn to their collection, continuing the trend towards fewer but larger business units. Since 1900 the number of slate firms in north Wales had shrunk from 100 to 36, their average output increasing from 4000 tons to well over 5000 tons per year.

In Dinbych things were steady, during the 20s and into the 30s 4000 tons or so was produced each year, mostly from Cambrian and Moel y Faen, each employing about 100 men. Most of the rest being raised by Clogau and West Llangynog with 20 or so men each. (Moellferna at that time being in Meirionnydd.) This was only half of the county's turn of the century total, but well up to what had come from there in much of the 19thC. Pembrokeshire's traditional few thousand tons, was down to a few hundreds, Montgomeryshire contributed a similar amount, but Cardiganshire, scarcely anything at all.

North west Wales tonnages did improve in 1934 with all the larger quarries restoring full-time working. In March, Dinorwig worked their first Saturday for 4 years. There was further improvement in 1935, Welsh tonnage reaching almost 230,000. Some very slight price increases were obtained, and some small wage rises granted[4]. Alexandra, having closed for some months, re-opened with new machinery, Garreg Fawr was revived, and an attempt was made to resuscitate nearby Plas y Nant after 40 years of idleness. There was even activity at such little slab workings as Gartheiniog.

However, the overall outlook was not good. In 1922 annual house completions had numbered 103,000 in 1935 they were 332,000 a rise of over 200%. Over the same period slate consumption had increased by only 25%. Whereas in 1922 almost half of new houses had slate roofs, by 1935 the proportion had fallen to well under 20%. For besides the cost of roofing with tiles being less, slate was unfashionably redolent of the old industrial terraces, and out of keeping with the smart new suburbias. Also apartment blocks and 'modernistic' houses, both with flat roofs were being built in increasing numbers. Even local loyalties were stretched, as when Pembrokeshire County Council opted for tiles. It being calculated that the heavy local slate, though no dearer would have called for an extra £7-8 per house in additional timbering.

Although a 15% duty had cut imports, in 1935 they still totalled 32,000 tons, over 500%, up on 1922. Possibly more worrying was the fact that quarries elsewhere in the U.K. were gaining ground. In 1922 when the Welsh output was about 200,000 tons, the rest of the U.K. produced little more than 30,000 tons, a 13% market share. By 1935 a demand for the 'fancy' colours from Westmorland[5] and recent vigorous activity by other English and Scottish producers, had pushed their tonnages to 70,000, a 23% market share. Exports, including Ireland, were little more than 3000 tons and falling.

By 1935 the decline of the granite trade having forced the Glyn Valley tramroad to close, Cambrian, with a tonnage nearing 3000 were now dispatching it all by road. The motor-lorry had become cheap and reliable and the 1930 Road Traffic Act having increased speed limits, its challenge to rail and to what remained of the coastwise shipping, was firmly established and growing.

Total U.K. tonnages edged downwards in 1936, to under 300,000 but a strong showing in Blaenau helped Wales a little against this trend. In 1937 U.K. tonnages eased again with Scottish and Isle of Man quarries being badly hit, but again thanks to a good showing in Blaenau despite some industrial problems, Welsh tonnage at 226,000 held up well.

The industry was becoming even more concentrated, with Dinorwig, Blaenau and Penrhyn accounting for about 80% of the output. Nantlle, where employment was little more than half its early 1931 total, produced about 10%. The other 10% came from the rest of north and mid Wales. South west Wales had by now virtually vanished, Twrch quarry's last substantial order before closure being the roofing of Carmarthen County Hall.

The highlight of 1937 was the Coronation, as royal occasion have always been celebrated with some enthusiasm in the slate areas. It was a public holiday, quarries such as Penrhyn paying an extra 10/ (50p) to the men and 5/ (25p) to the boys and almost for the last time, Rock Cannon were fired. These Rock Cannon were used to celebrate notable events, both local and national. They comprised a number of holes drilled in a flat rock, with incised channels connecting them. Properly charged with powder these would provide a succession of explosions. Examples survive at Blaenau, Llanberis, Croesor, Rhiwbach, Cwm Eigiau and a number in Dyffryn Ogwen. It is said that some were capable of 'playing' God Save the Queen. (Recent experiments have failed to produce any such recognisable cadence.)

But after the high jinks it was back to the grind, in a shrunken and ailing industry, clinging to a minority share of a market it had dominated little more than a quarter of a century before. The still primitive state of affairs was exemplified, when in the dry summer of 1938, Bryneglwys had to conserve water by suspending the supply of electricity to the village of Abergynolwyn. Then with the reservoir dry and totally dependent on water power, all work had to stop to await the Autumn rains.

Thus when war came in 1939, the industry was smaller, weaker and in worse shape to meet its difficulties, than it had been in 1914.

[1] Before the end of 1915, long before the introduction of conscription, well under a year after the first war-time volunteers would have completed training, hundreds of Welsh quarrymen had become casualties. Although their skills would have been welcomed in the Royal Engineers, the majority were in the Royal Welch Fusiliers, one of the 'Minden' regiments whose distinguished traditions can be traced back to Agincourt. Their losses in France were heavy even by WW1 standards, it is believed that no industry of comparable size, suffered as many dead in WW1 as did the slate industry. Nor were losses confined to the men, many owners and their relatives died, including Sir Robin Duff, heir to Sir Charles Assheton-Smith, who was killed in November 1915, just 3 weeks after Sir Charles' death. One of the Darbishires of Pen yr Orsedd was also killed.

[2] The North Wales Quarry Owners Association, included; Amalgamated Slate (Alexandra, Cilgwyn & Moel Tryfan), Pen yr Orsedd, Dorothea, South Dorothea, Pen y Bryn, Tal y Sarn, Diffwys & Rhosydd; plus Penrhyn and Dinorwig who had joined during the war. The Ffestiniog & District Quarry Proprietors Association included; Manod, Graig Ddu and Rhiwbach. Greaves (Llechwedd), Oakeley, Maenofferen, Parc & Croesor, and Votty & Bowydd, belonged to both. The two organisations amalgamated in the early 1930s.

[3] In the mid 1930s Penrhyn quarry calculated that for all purposes, they utilised 3760 hp of electric power, 1740 hp of steam, 1090 of hydro power and 200 hp from oil-engines. This equalled 3 hp per man employed. The average for all quarries at the time was 2 hp per man employed.

[4] These wage increases which brought the minimum wage up from 7/3 (agreed at Arbitration in 1932) to 7/6 (36.25p-37.5p). This gave minimum weekly earnings of about £2.00. With a Letting Standard at a maximum of 9/9 (48.75) the top rockmen averaged just under £3.00 for a full week. It is interesting to see the contrast with white-collar pay at the time. A court case involving falsification by two wages clerk at Penrhyn showed their salaries to be £300 and £260 p.a. respectively.

[5] A 'Colloidal Slate' factory at Deganwy coated slates in 'popular' colours. Such slates cost about 15% extra, but although they still underpriced the Westmorland product, they were not a success.

12. Nadir and a New Hope
1939 on

The outbreak of war in September 1939, brought an even more abrupt drop in trade than had 1914. Within weeks, Dinorwig closed their outliers, Allt Ddu and Vivian. Others such as Penrhyn, also closed departments, some like Dorothea closed completely. The rest ticked over, most working short time, hoping for the best. Bryneglwys kept going but suffered from a big collapse and flooding. In January 1940 Penrhyn shut down for 5 weeks, announcing that they would not be able to re-employ single men aged between 20 and 35. By this time the industry was described as '*In severe depression, with large stocks of unsold product*'. The many buildings furiously being erected for military purposes might have provided an outlet, but these were invariably roofed in other materials, some of which it was claimed, were imported.

Many quarries were to play a direct part in the war effort, the Glynrhonwys became an ordnance factory and a depot, Dinorwig's extensive workshops turned out munition components. Underground chambers in idle quarries such as Croesor, Wynne, Llanfair and Hendre Ddu (Dinas Mawddwy), were ideal for explosives storage, the latter's tramway being replaced by a road to facilitate this. Bwlch y Slaters held works of art and even abandoned chambers at still-working quarries such as Braich Goch kept munitions hidden. Defence factories were again established at Bethesda and elsewhere. Ports built landing craft. As men left to man these and other war industries or to join the forces more quarries closed. Others struggled on with scratch crews of the old, the unfit and the very young, Government restrictions confining their markets to emergency bomb damage repairs. By 1945 tonnage was scarcely 70,000, and of the prewar total of 40 quarries, less than 20 remained open.

The end of the war brought a demand for slates to re-roof blitzed buildings but their use, except in very small sizes, was banned for new construction. This meant that there was no repeat of the unbridled scramble of 1918-1920, but the run-down quarries could scarcely cope with even this constrained market. Continuing price controls means that they could neither afford to re-equip, nor pay realistic wages.

There were also controls on virtually everything the quarries needed to buy, timber, steel, motor fuel, coal and so on, were all in 'short supply', obtainable, if at all, only on permit. More serious was the manpower shortage. Quarry workers were granted early release from the forces, and mercifully there were many more survivors than there had been from WW1, but now as then, the returning men often opted for better paid and less arduous employment. Several increases had brought wages well above prewar levels, the day rate being up from 9/4 (46p) to 14/10 (74p) with piecework rates perhaps 25% more, but in the meantime living costs had risen even further.

By Mid 1946 Dinorwig had only managed to build up to about 1300 men, well under half their prewar numbers, and not much more than their wartime low of 1000. Increasingly difficult working conditions with obsolete plant and an ageing workforce, reduced their productivity to only 22 tons per man. At Penrhyn things were worse, where 1000 men were needed to raise about 20,000 tons. Nantlle, with only 350 men at work in the whole district, virtually ceased to be a significant slate area. At Blaenau, Diffwys, Votty & Bowydd, Rhiw Bach and Cwt y Bugail were all turning out only a fraction of their former tonnages. Oakeley, Llechwedd and Maenofferen remained the only substantial producers. The whole of the Welsh industry barely topped 100,000 tons, less than half the prewar figure and not dramatically above war-time output.

Controlled prices were raised in 1946 by a derisory 2½% and the next year by 5%. This made scant contribution to parlous finances, and was almost entirely absorbed by a wage award of 5/6 (27.5p) per week, and a reduction in working hours to 44. With even top men averaging little over £5, there certainly was no stampede for quarry jobs. In early 1947, the Cambrian quarry at Glyn Ceiriog, had to lay off their 70 men due to severe weather, many obtaining temporary work clearing snow. Having sampled such seemingly light and highly paid work, so few chose to return that the quarry could not re-open. Similarly, when there were strikes later that year, a number of men obtained other employment.

It was becoming clear that little Government help could be expected. For example, agricultural workers and miners, received priority in housing, but underground slatemen were not officially classed as 'miners' for this purpose, in spite of their workplaces being legally defined as mines. Similarly, food being still rationed, coal miners got special allocations of such things as cheese, slate 'miners' did not.

In 1947 controls were relaxed to permit slate roofing on new buildings within Wales and in England if not more than 75 miles from the source quarry. This brought talk of re-activating some old sites such as Pantmawr and Parc, there was even a proposal to re-open Gorseddau! With manning so difficult, plant expensive and scarce, and with no one coming forward to invest in slate, none of these enterprises came about.

All restrictions on slate supplies were lifted in 1949, but the quarries were unable to make much impact on the tile dominated market. Many quarries could not match even wartime manpower levels, and some, such as Bryneglwys, which had survived the vicissitudes of a century or more, not to speak of two wars, stumbled into closure. Several quarries were advertising surplus equipment, among them Moelfferna, hawking their incline gear, rollers, and tramway track, which the use of lorries had made redundant.

The 1951 election was largely won on promises of an unprecedented house-building programme and unlike many election promises, these were substantially fulfilled, but overwhelmingly the roofs were tiled. In 1952, even in Caernarfon, municipal housing was being tiled. Since this showed a saving of £100 per house, and with local authorities under pressure to contain costs, an understandable policy. Not only costs were involved, as again, big building schemes demanded large quantities to a standard specification, which the now booming tile industry could and did provide. Such slate demand as there was,

was being increasingly met by imports from Continental sources. In the late 1940s, only neutral Portugal had been able to export, but by the early 1950s countries such as France and Italy, recovering from war-time devastation, had surpluses. The Press fulminated about the poor quality of imported slate, but although there was some truth in this, buyers were not deterred.

Trifling incidents were hailed as harbingers of resurgence, such as the 1953 loading of 100 tons of Moel Tryfan slate at Caernarfon, the first slate dispatched by sea since before the war. But the slide in sales continued with stocks starting to accumulate, particularly of the smaller sizes and Damp Course slates[1]. The slab trade was all but non-existent, at best 2% or 3% of output.

From the early 1950s demand slipped year by year, but in spite of severe unemployment problems in the slate districts, most quarries were still constrained by lack of men, rather than lack of orders. In 1955 the once great Diffwys finally closed, just failing to reach its bicentential. By 1956 several pay rises had brought the labourer's day rate to £6 19 6 (£6.98) per week but the skilled men's day rate was only about 4/6 (23p) more. The effect of this was apparent the next year when Cwm Penmachno laid off 20 men of lower skills as they could not get enough Rockmen and Slatemakers to support them, shortly afterwards closing completely.

Neighbouring Rhiwbach besides having manning problems were tied to the use of the now rickety tramway. Having failed in their rather cheeky bid to get the Local Authority to repair their 'road' access, they too closed. Even with the 1960 increase of 5/ (25p) per week, wages were little more than young girls were being offered in the factories now coming to the area. Plus of course factories provided dry, heated workplaces, good washing and lavatory facilities, and canteens. Certainly much better money was to be had on construction work such as the Trawsfynydd and Tanygrisiau power stations, the Tryweryn dam and in plants such as Llanwern in south Wales.

Moelfferna where Thomas Firbank writing in 1952 quoted the manager T.J. Davies as saying '*I could employ 200 men but can only get 27*', rumbled on quite profitably but by 1960 the impossibility of finding skilled replacements for their tiny and ageing workforce made closure inevitable.

Annual sales already down to 50,000 tons drifted down further, with employment well under 2000, half of what it had been 10 years earlier. Prices at over 3 times prewar figures were approaching levels at which efficient units could profitably operate, but widened the gap between slate and tile. Also, slum-clearance and urban renewal schemes provided an abundant source of second-hand slates, their much vaunted durability thus now proving highly counterproductive. Demand for the smaller sizes all but vanished, resulting in a further accumulation of stocks which the widening of price differentials failed to move.

Decades of hand to mouth working had left most quarries in a disorganised mess, overwhelmed with ill-sited rubbish tips, they struggled with out-of-date methods and worn out plant. None more so than the once mighty Dinorwig. Still using traditional saws, (although most of their 500 tables were idle.) Still using some steam locos, gulping prohibitively priced coal, having only pensioned off the last of their horses in the early 1950s. With only 700 men remaining and an almost negligible output, they energetically revived their 1930s Marchlyn ideas. At the new Marchlyn Mawr site, almost at the top of the mountain, reputedly a million and a half tons of overburden was cleared by the most modern machinery. New saws were put in to cope with the optimistically predicted 12,000 ton output, but it all proved a costly failure, (ultimately obliterated by the top reservoir of the pumped storage scheme). Encouraged by some firming of demand in the mid 60s they hung on. The almost total cessation of dispatches by sea, (their last steamship having been sold in 1955, the same year that Penrhyn disposed of their sole surviving vessel) and lorries replacing rail freight, made the Padarn railway redundant and in 1961 it was closed. A year later the Penrhyn line was also closed, and a year after that, the still horse-drawn Nantlle tramway took its last load from Pen yr Orsedd. On a shrinking market the contraction inexorably continued.

In 1967 prices were reduced, but Best Duchesses still cost about

£170 per 1000, which worked out at £1.75 per sq/yd, way over any other roofing material. Some attempts were made to re-develop the market for slate for flooring and for large decorative items such as coffee-tables, but cost limited the scope for these. More success was achieved, and is still being achieved, with small knick-knacks and souveniers. These, though involving negligible tonnages, are a high 'added-value' product particularly as they can often be made from waste materials.

By 1969 the total Welsh output was only 25% of that of 20 years earlier, little more than half the UK requirement for building repairs alone. With no let up in sight, Dinorwig bowed to the inevitable and sacked their remaining 350 men.

In the meantime, Dorothea had been boldly modernising. In 1955 a 60 hp electric pump, (plus another for stand-by), had replaced the Holman beam engine. These pumps, operating at night on off-peak rates, dewatered only to 440'. The sinc below this level being used solely for waste, thus eliminating some uphaulage. A road was built down into the workings, enabling agricultural tractors and trailers loaded by mechanical shovel to handle both block and waste. Rail movements, along with their solitary horse, were phased out. One of their 20 Greaves type saws was converted into a diamond saw of their own devising by Williams of Porthmadog. Its 10hp motor and 20″ blade travelled above and across the existing table enabling the table-motion to be used to position the block for cutting. A small pulverising plant was also commissioned. Yet in spite of having invested some £25,000, by 1969 with annual tonnage under 1000 and falling, they too were forced to close.

The next year Oakeley, the largest of all underground workings succumbed, in part due to the ever increasing costs of pumping. Smaller operations such as Rhos and Votty & Bowydd had already closed, Cwt y Bugail and Moel Tryfan staggered on for a time before they too closed. In 1969 Pen yr Orsedd, down to 30 men with an output of only 700 tons, perceived that with so many competitors having failed, there was a prospect of survival, provided that methods were radically updated. They put in 3

Anderson Grice Diamond saws, 2 with 600mm blades, hand fed (the operator moved the table in accordance with the ammeter read-out from the 20hp motor), and one with a 450mm blade, hydraulically fed. They also had a locally made 600mm saw, for the department producing floor tiles 12″ x 12″ x 3/8 and wall tiles 4″ x 4″ x 1/4. All waste being dealt with by conveyor. They later built a road down to the workings, making the last surviving Blondins in the industry redundant, but by the late 1970s with only 15 men still employed, they too closed. By now, less than 20,000 tons of Welsh slate could find a market, mostly produced by one quarry, Penrhyn. Even the tip-pickers[2] found their gleanings unprofitable.

At Blaenau only the Greaves company carried on, probably cross-subsidised by their Quarry Tours venture. This successful enterprise, based around the old Llechwedd No 2 mill, capitalised on a long tradition of quarries as 'tourist attractions'. According to A.T. Story, writing in the 1890's '*A courteous application to managers will generally result in permission being given to go over the quarries*'. So popular were these visits that at one time Penrhyn retained a retired slateman as a guide. Unfortunately regulations now restrict visits to working quarries.

At Corris, Llwyngwern faded away (becoming the site for the Centre for Alternative Technology) and Braich Goch, a shadow of its former glory, just quietly died, to be re-incarnated as a cafe and craft-centre, and eventually as a Theme Cavern. Aberllefenni soldiered on solely as a slab producer. Apart from some very small scale working in the Nantlle valley, at Berwyn and at Cwmorthin, that was it. (Cwmorthin was worked underground, transport being provided by an old Landrover whose dents testified to the narrowness of the passages through which it was driven. It is a sad reflection on our times that due to vandalism their saw had to be re-sited in an underground chamber).

The industry was locked into a downward spiral, with outputs, manpower and stocks at such an ebb that producers could not respond to orders when they came. Users could not rely on being able to get Welsh slate in the sizes and quantities, and at the time they needed it. Even the most sympathetic Planning Authorities had to waive their insistence on local product. By the early 1970s total employment had fallen to little more than 500. Towns such as Blaenau Ffestiniog, their populations halved, their shops shuttered, their hopes shattered, were, like the industry that had created them, gripped in an abomination of decay.

Those quarries not vanishing under the bland grasses of 'landscaping' schemes, or the conifers of afforestation, seemed destined to be just sources of landfill hardcore. Their only likely product being the slates stripped from their abandoned buildings, or of slates cut from the blocks of the buildings themselves. The best hope seeming to be to become part of the tourist scene with Visitor Centres such as, Llechwedd, Llanfair, Wynne, and later, Gloddfa Ganol.

It had been said of Penrhyn 1880 *'The peculiar metallic sound emitted as the slates shoot down the steep inclines, the oft-recurring reverberations from the blasting, the enormous sombre heaps of rubbish, the materials of which are ever restless, ever working, the Babel of Welsh tongues shouting and vociferating as only a Welshman can shout, the ceaseless bustle'*. Now it seemed that such sounds would only be heard as electronic simulations.

Then, in the early 1980s there came a turnaround. The grants to restore old houses stimulated demand for slate. At the same time there was a growing appreciation of its properties which caused architects to increasingly specify it for both roofing and detail of commercial and public buildings as well as more prestigious houses. Also and vitally, the soaring fuel prices of the mid 1970s had forced up the cost of kiln firing and hence tile prices, thus enabling slate prices to be advanced to levels which could make quarrying economically viable. And at last, and almost too late, Government grants became more readily available to help quarries re-equip to meet this new demand.

There had already been two bold initiatives which augured well for the future, both in a sense backward integrations, similar to some in the past. In 1956 the Lloyd brothers, seeking sources for their London slate enamelling interests, bought Braich Goch and Aberllefenni, and although they had to eventually abandon the former, they vigorously modernised the latter. Meanwhile at Penrhyn, the fourth Baron Penrhyn having died in 1949, the estate passed to his niece Lady Janet Douglas-Pennant who disposed of much of the non-quarry property the next year. (Caemaes estate which comprised much of the rest of Bethesda had been sold off in 1947.) With the quarry output dwindling, she passed part ownership and management to the McAlpine construction group in 1964, selling out completely in 1973.

Although these ventures differed greatly in scale, they were both unencumbered by any great experience of Welsh slate quarrying. To both proprietors the fact something had 'always been done this or that way', was, in view of the industry's decline, seen as good grounds for considering alternative approaches.

At Aberllefenni, the product to waste ratio which had been running at a profligate 1 to 67 was cut back to 1-3, largely thanks to the pioneering use of a Korfmann chain saw. This saw, which had been developed in Germany during the war, was virtually unknown in the U.K. until it came to prominence when it was used in the re-siting of the Abu Simbel temple in Upper Egypt. Later the chainsaw was supplemented by a wiresaw. Handling was updated and the mill equipped not only with diamond saws, but also with a reciprocating diamond gang-saw. Efficiency of production of their premium slab was further improved in the 1980s, when their finishing processes were moved from Caernarfon to Aberllefenni.

At Penrhyn, one of the first actions by the new management was to rid themselves of the constraints of the internal rail system. Euclids loaded by diggers carried rubble and fork trucks handled block. Later a system of tractors and semitrailers was put in to maintain a constant supply of block to the mills. Abandoning rails, apart from the obvious advantages of being able to move material more quickly, also greatly simplifies development work. It also enables much larger blocks to be carried to the mill, fully exploiting the capacity of modern saws. The mills were rebuilt and re-equipped, eventually having conveyor-fed, paired diamond saws with laser measurement to optimise block out-turn, and with all waste handled by belts. Some traditional chiselling is still needed in the mill to divide block, but in the quarry this is done by 'woodpeckers' mounted on hydraulic arms of tractors.

Penrhyn were one of the first quarries to palettise all finished slate, which together with restriction of the product range enabled high productivities to be achieved. Make to waste ratio has remained something of a problem, partly because of energetic extraction methods and partly because the best rock is overlaid by inferior material. Efforts to improve this by sawing rock from the face proved disappointing. Penrhyn now accounts for almost 50% of U.K. production, a market dominance far beyond the Penrhyn dynasty's wildest expectations, and far exceeding the UK's second largest quarry, Burlington in Cumbria.

At Llechwedd too, well ahead of any sign of recovery, manager B. Hefin Davies, (later becoming the first non-family member to head up the Greaves company), staunchly maintained his belief that slate quarrying had a future. Under Hefin y Ffydd (Hefin of the Faith) Llechwedd was extensively modernised. Instead of 4 mills with 100 saw tables, reduction was concentrated at No 5 mill, with diamond saws being installed in the 1960s. Afterwards No 7 mill was re built and re-equipped with winched trolley-fed saws (where all work is now done). They took in Votty & Bowydd and Diffwys where, as at Llechwedd itself, the untopping methods they pioneered in the 1930s were energetically pursued. Excavators, Euclids and forklifts replaced manhandling and all use of rails, (the main incline being last used in 1964). Shot-firing was supplemented by crawler-mounted jack-hammers and wiresawing.

Maenofferen, owned by J.W. Greaves in the 1850s, was bought back in 1952 and is still worked underground, with wiresaws also being used for extraction, rubbish in the chambers being handled by excavator. Reduction is carried out in the now modernised mill. In 1976 a new road made redundant the Rhiwbach No 2 incline, the last self-acting incline in Wales. Rail is still used underground, the haulage inclines being operated by the original electric machinery, controlled by Brine Bath resistors. Though the number Greaves employ on production is less than a quarter of the heyday peak it is some four times the 35 of the 1960s.

At Blaenau there were also other happenings. A notable figure in the industry in the inter-war years and a founder member of the Institute of Mines and Quarries, had been T.O. Williams. The son of a Blaenau quarryman who had been killed at Cesail quarry, T.O. had been manager at Aberllefenni and had operated various quarries on his own account, such as Llanfair, Wrysgan and Braich Goch (with Abercorris), his enterprise not always achieving the success it deserved. His son, T. Glyn Williams, after briefly being involved at Hendre Ddu (Dinas Mawddwy) in the late 1930s, had built up a successful contracting and plant hire business. In 1970 Glyn and his sons boldly bought the Oakeley quarry site, not only as a base for their existing business, but also to restart slate working. This they did at Lower Quarry, (the old Welsh Slate Co. site), trading as the Ffestiniog Slate Company. The rest of the site was hived off to Glyn's son-in-law, Will Roberts who opened up the Gloddfa Ganol Visitor Centre and also made craft objects from waste material from the Lower Quarry. Later Gloddfa Ganol commenced their own extraction and the production of roofing slates and slab. Significantly, any shortage of experience in the slate industry was more than compensated by a great knowledge of plant and machinery and ingenuity in its adaption. Subsequently the Cwt y Bugail company was acquired, and although the quarry of that name has not yet been worked, the company was used as a springboard for the notable lawsuit which resulted in the Department of the Environment yielding its hold on the Bwlch y Slaters quarry, which then became available for them to fully develop along with the Graig Ddu site. They also acquired Pen yr Orsedd where they trade as the Nantlle Slate Company. New mills were built at the Blaenau quarries, and the Pen yr Orsedd mill was re-equipped, all have diamond saws and other modern machinery. In 1991 the Cwt y Bugail company opened a highly automated 'tile' factory at Bwlch y Slaters. There, slate is cut into thin slab, passes on a conveyor to be trimmed to width, surface polished, edged and cut to length for cladding and flooring. They also have a profiling

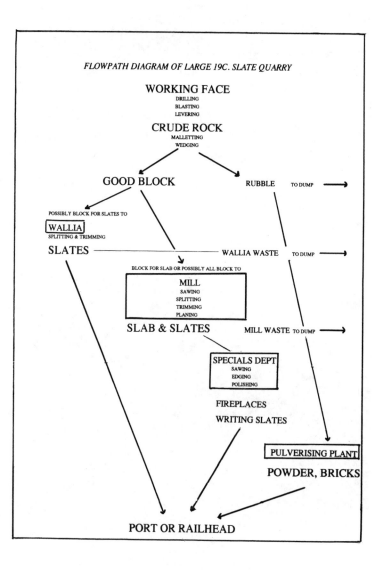

FLOWPATH DIAGRAM OF LARGE 19C. SLATE QUARRY

WORKING FACE
DRILLING
BLASTING
LEVERING

CRUDE ROCK
MALLETTING
WEDGING

GOOD BLOCK   **RUBBLE**   TO DUMP →

POSSIBLY BLOCK FOR SLATES TO

WALLIA
SPLITTING & TRIMMING

SLATES ——— **WALLIA WASTE**   TO DUMP →

BLOCK FOR SLAB OR POSSIBLY ALL BLOCK TO

MILL
SAWING
SPLITTING
TRIMMING
PLANING

SLAB & SLATES   MILL WASTE   TO DUMP →

SPECIALS DEPT
SAWING
EDGING
POLISHING

FIREPLACES

WRITING SLATES

PULVERISING PLANT

POWDER, BRICKS

PORT OR RAILHEAD

Bwlch y Slaters 1994
Authors collection

Handling block, Blaenau Ffestiniog 1890s?
By permission Gwynedd Archives Service

Greaves type saw table, Llechwedd
By kind permission of J.W. Greaves & Sons Ltd

Demonstration of hand slate trimming
North Wales Slate Quarrying Museum
Author's collection

SH620640 +

Penrhyn Slate Quarries

Quarter Mile

D   E   G   A   1

Penrhyn, c 1985
Author's collection

De Winton Dressing Machine, Penrhyn 1985
Author's collection

Barracks at Gelli 1994
Author's collection

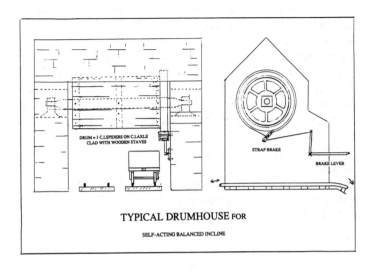

TYPICAL DRUMHOUSE FOR

SELF-ACTING BALANCED INCLINE

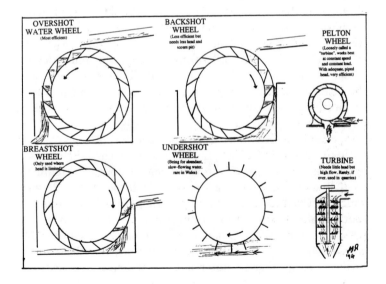

machine to produce shaped plaques etc. Up-to-date mechanical handling is employed at all sites and the Blaenau quarries are worked by untopping.

Regrettably, in 1985 the vigour with which the Williams quarries were modernised, gave rise to dispute. There followed a seven month strike, the first of any consequence in Blaenau for over 90 years and the longest dispute in the industry since the turn of the century events at Penrhyn. Confrontations were robust, but never ugly. However heated the negotiations, (always in Welsh, of course), the friendly 'ti' form of address was invariably used, never the more formal 'chi'.

Fortunately the divisions at Blaenau healed more quickly than at Bethesda, where almost a century after 1900-1903, the descendants of 'Y Bradwyr' (The Traitors) who worked during the strike, are still regarded with some suspicion. But it was a setback for the town and the industry.

A spin off from the strike was the re-opening of Croes y Ddwy Afon after 60 years of idleness, by a group of dismissed workers. To augment their locally based financing they obtained apparently strong outside supporters, who also took an interest in Cwmorthin. Their untopping and mill modernisation enabled them to prosper, even getting at least one order from the USA which included the installation of the slates. Unfortunately the 1990s recession caused their backers to fail. Though Croes y Ddwy Afon remains idle, at Cwmorthin, a new company has been formed to resume working on a much enhanced scale.

At Nantlle the Humphreys carry on their two centuries of family tradition at the little Twll Llwyd quarry. There, though their extraction replicates 18thC crow-barring methods, all handling is by JCB, and reduction by a locally made diamond saw. Berwyn, which survived for years as a tiny working, was taken over by a south Wales businessman in the early 1990s, to develop its potential for slab production. Although environmental considerations can pose difficulties, it is likely that there will be further re-openings, untopping abandoned underground workings.

Conditions in present day quarrying are far removed from those of only a few decades ago. Men travel by car or by crew bus to work for rewards comparable with other occupations. Clothing protects them from the wet and from minor injury, and machinery has eliminated the worst of the toil. Dust control has abated dust diseases. No longer are men required to hang from ropes or chains, or to work by candlelight under doubtful roofs, so accidents are now rare. No longer do we have scenes such as used to occur at Dinorwig. Where, when the locomotive whistles signalled an accident, people in Llanberis would rush into the streets to stare across the lake as the stretcher made its long and laborious journey down gallery after gallery to the quarry hospital. And then, watch to see if it would be taken in through the front doors or continue on to the slate-tabled mortuary. Easier and safer though it may be, modern slate quarrying is still an arduous, challenging and skilled occupation. No matter how mechanised, the old arts are still called Apart from the actual splitting of roofing slates, blocks still have to be divided by blows delivered with as much skill (and with almost as much value at stake) as that of a gemstone worker.

Slate will always be vulnerable to competition from sources where rock is cheaply obtainable by large-scale opencasting. Imports which in the 1960s had drifted down to almost token quantities, took an increasing share from the mid 1970s. In 1990 out of a total U.K. market of 85,000 tons, 43,000 was imported, much of it from Spain, at prices at least 25% lower than the ruling £1000 per ton for best Welsh roofing slate[3]. The early 1990s apart from seeing a reduction in demand, also saw even cheaper products being offered from low wage areas such as Brazil and China.

From whatever source, slate will always be competing head on with other roofing materials, which will tend to set a price ceiling. Although productivities are, thanks to modern machinery, double the traditional 30 or so tons per man year, capital amortisation even spread by 2 or 3 shift working, imposes heavy overheads. Further technical advances will undoubtedly reduce the labour-intensiveness of slate quarrying, but increased automation is likely to correspondingly reduce tile factory costs. Skilfully sliced up bits of natural rock are bound to be dearer than process-generated products. The acknowledged durability of slate, particularly Welsh slate, is no longer such a great factor. Few building specifiers are likely to be swayed by a life prediction measured in centuries and anyway slate's advantages of durability may be eroded as improvements in substitute materials are made. Due to its lighter weight it can offer some economies in roof construction, but this is only appreciable in large spans. Tiling is quicker and less skilled than slating, and although the difference has been narrowed by offering 'pre-holed' slates, tiles still retain an installation cost advantage. Slate has a further, inherent problem. To be economic, qualities, sizes and production volumes, have to be governed by the nature of the most accessible rock, not by what the market is currently demanding. This and the ability to meet large orders, even when output is slowed by bad rock or re-development, calls for very large quantities being put down as stock, either by the quarry, a stockist or an end-user. Modern 'Just in Time, Not Just in Case' business economics discourage this. A tile manufacturer does not have these problems. Also he can rapidly, change moulds or mixes, he can put on extra shifts and can afford to lay off semi-skilled machine operators. A slate-producer apart from being tied to rock availability, cannot easily or quickly augment his skilled labour force, nor can such men be allowed to leave with impunity, Roofing slate is, and must remain, a premium prestige product.

As far as slab is concerned, costs bar Welsh material from any non appearance-sensitive application, such as billiards tables beds. This latter trade has long been an Italian speciality, partly because of the traditional use of cheap female labour and because of its lighter weight. However, the best Welsh slab has an unique appeal for cladding, flooring and building detail, as well as for plaques and so on, which no other material can quite equal.

In some respects the slate industry has been forced back a couple of centuries as, except where enforced by planning requirements, it once again has to find its clientele from amongst the wealthy. Fortunately, there are world-wide, increasing numbers of individuals and organisations who can afford the best and modern communications are making them aware that Welsh slate is the best. Today's re-invigorated industry is penetrating markets such as the Middle East, undreamt of in the past.

If slate is ever to again become a fully competitive roofing material, slate making will probably have to become a de-skilled factory process via pulverisation and reconstitution.

Finding uses for the millions of tons of slate waste has occupied minds for 2 centuries. In 1812 the French claimed to be able to pulverise it to make blocks, and throughout the 19thC. there were reports of weird and wonderful uses which could be made of it. Powdered slate for a variety of purposes has almost from the earliest days, been a significant part of Penrhyn output, although they have never been able to dispose of more than 1% of their total waste in this way. Other quarries have long had, at least a minor trade in it, with varying degrees of success. In 1919 the North Wales Development Company was set up at Bethesda to make powder at Pantdreiniog. Although they processed some 100 tons per week, some as 'Myrtox' for metal-cleaning, by the end of 1922 they were insolvent. Hafod Las when it was reactivated in 1919 included a pulverising plant, but the quarry closed ten years later. Glogue's 1920 brick making plant closed after only 7 years, reputedly due to the railways' ceasing to classify their product as building brick, which was carried at reduced rates. In 1949 a plant at Porthmadog to make tiles from Nantlle tips failed to meet expectations. Dinorwig's 1954 brick and tile plant, initially produced with two shift working, some 50,000 bricks per day, but failed to recoup the large investment. Likewise the unsuccessful 1954 brick making plant at Llwyngwern and the abortive Corris Fillers, pulverising plant at Braich Goch four years later. Pulverised slate has been used for cement making, (such as the Solite plant at Bwlchgwyn, Wrexham in the 1960s, which used tip material from the Oernant quarries), as an abrasive, for compacting into insulators etc., as a filler for linoleum and plastics, as source of mineral wool and for glass making, even for face powder.

Many attempts have also been made to create artificial 'slates' by this route, and as early as 1920 some limited success was reported from the USA. Now, at last, with the development of suitable resin binders, satisfactory products are feasible. These are mainly in two types, one is an interlocking tile, the other a replication of a natural slate, which from ground level is indistinguishable from the genuine article. In the 1980s a pulverising plant was installed at the Ffestiniog Slate Company's site to produce powder for moulding into 'slates' in south Wales. Although there are contamination problems when working old tips, if newly made rubble is used, the results seem to be both technically and commercially successful.

Regrettably, indications are that if further 'slate factories' are established few, if any, will be sited in the quarrying districts. Even if they are, like the plastics and light assembly plants of recent years, they will not replicate the proud ethos of the quarries.

But one does see that the old traditions are not lightly abandoned. Though no longer has every quarry its band, every gallery its choir and every caban its poet, the musical and literary heritage they nurtured still continues. There are even places in north-west Wales where shop hours still conform to the worktimes of long abandoned quarries. Most proudly, in parts of north Caernarfonshire, all business comes to a standstill on Ascension Day, honouring a holiday the old slatemen fought for so long ago.

---

[1] Damp Course slates are still listed, priced at around half the price of 'roofing' slates. They are thicker and may be uneven. Though few are used for their original purpose they represent a useful economy in non appearance sensitive applications, and for matching old work may sometimes be preferable.

[2] There is a long tradition for the tips of abandoned quarries to be picked over for likely pieces for making slates (with or without permission!). In Dyffryn Nantlle, especially, it was the custom for working quarries, to allow this, buying in the slates the pickers produced. The remains of these tip-pickers crude shelters and some of the slates they made, can still be found on the tips.

[3] Slate prices in 1900 were approximately four times those of 1800. In 1960 they were 11 times that of 1900. By the early 1990s they were almost 25 times the 1960 levels (plus VAT!).

Appendix 1
Grid References of Quarries in Text

O = Open air
U = Underground
M = Mechanised

Aber	SH977594	Dinbych	O Very Small
Abereiddi	SM798314	Fishguard	O Very Small
Abercorris	SH754089	Corris	U Moderate M
Abercwmeiddaw	SH746093	Corris	O Moderate M
Aberdunant	SH583420	Tremadoc	U Very Small M
Aberllefenni	SH768103	Corris	U Large M
Afon Wen	SH678663	Bethesda	O Very Small
Alexandra	SH519562	Penygroes	O Moderate M
Allt Ddu	SH591610	Llanberis	O Moderate M
Alltgoch	SN620964	Aberdyfi	U Small M
Arddu	SH594576	Llanberis	U Very Small
Arthog	SH652152	Dolgellau	O Moderate M
Beaver Pool	SH797552	Betws y Coed	O Very Small
Berthllwyd	SH629481	Beddgelert	O Small M
Berwyn	See Clogau		
Blaen y Cae	SH498535	Penygroes	O Small M
Blaen y Cwm	SH735459	Bl. Ffestiniog	O & U Moderate M
Bowydd	SH708464	Bl. Ffestiniog	U Large M
Braich	SH510552	Penygroes	O Small M
Braich Ddu	SH718384	Ffestiniog	O Small M
Braich Goch	SH748078	Corris	U Large M
Braich Rhyd	SH512548	Penygroes	O Small M
Brithdir	SJ126223	Llanfyllin	O Very Small M
Brondanw Isaf	SH616421	Llanfrothen	O Very Small
Brondanw Uchaf	SH619426	Llanfrothen	O Very Small
Brongarnedd	SH620426	Llanfrothen	O Very Small
Brongoronwy	SH729414	Ffestiniog	O Very Small
Bron y Foel	SH544390	Porthmadog	O Very Small
Bryneglwys	SH695054	Towyn	U Very Large M
Brynfferam	SH519558	Penygroes	O Small M
Bryngelynen	SH634437	Llanfrothen	O Very Small M

Bryngwyn	SH627133	Fairbourne	O Small
Brynmawr	SH555595	Llanberis	O Small
Bryn Hafod y Wern	SH631693	Bethesda	O Small M
Bwlch Cwm Llan	SH600521	Beddgelert	O Small M
Bwlch Gwyn	SH767558	Betws y Coed	U Small M
Bwlch y Ddwy Elor	SH557500	Caernarfon	O Small
Bwlch y Slaters	SH732455	Bl. Ffestiniog	U Moderate M
Cae Abaty	SH846136	Dinas Mawddwy	O Very Small
Cae Madog	SH825654	Llanrwst	O Very Small M
Cae'n y Coed	SH681408	Ffestiniog	O Very Small
Cae'r Defaid	SH784233	Towyn	U Very Small
Caermenciau	SH562601	Llanberis	O Small
Cambergi	SH765108	Corris	O Small M
Cambrian	SH566603	Llanberis	O Small M
Cambrian (Glyn)	SJ189378	Chirk	O & U Mod'te M
Cedryn	SH719635	Dolgarrog	O Small M
Cefn Du	SH555604	Llanberis	O Moderate M
Cefn Gam	SH680256	Dolgellau	O Small M
Cefn y Braich	SH646448	Llanfrothen	O Very Small
Cesail	SH690466	Bl. Ffestiniog	U Very Large M
Chwarel Ddu	SH721521	Dolwyddelan	O Very Small M
Chwarel Fawr	SH552600	Llanberis	O Small M
Cilgwyn	SH500540	Penygroes	O Large M
Cletwr	SH985348	Bala	O Small M
Cloddfa'r Coed	SH493532	Penygroes	O Small M
Cloddfa'r Lon	See Penybryn		
Clogau	SJ185463	Llangollen	O Small M
Clogwyn y Fuwch	SH759618	Trefriw	U Small
Cnicht	SH643462	Llanfrothen	U Very Small
Coed Madog	SH490530	Penygroes	O Small M
Conglog	SH670467	Bl. Ffestiniog	U Small M
Cook	SH560605	Llanberis	O Small M
Craig Rhiwarth	SJ053262	Llangynog	O & U Mod'te M
Craig y Cribin	SJ047262	Llangynog	O & U Small
Craig y Glem	SJ171478	Llangollen	O Small M
Craig Wynnstay	SJ202473	Llangollen	O Small
Croesor	SH657457	Llanfrothen	O Large M
Croes y Ddwy Afon	SH754424	Ffestiniog	U Small M
Cwm Bach	SH564406	Tremadoc	O Small M

Cwm Brechiau	SH708043	Pennal	U Very Small M
Cwm Bychan	SH683655	Bethesda	U Very Small
Cwm Caeth	SH605466	Penrhynd'draeth	O Small M
Cwm Du	SH831125	Dinas Mawddwy	O Very Small
Cwm Dwyfor	SH541505	Tremadoc	U Very Small
Cwm Ebol	SH689017	Pennal	O Small M
Cwm Eigiau	SH701634	Dolgarrog	O Small M
Cwm Gloddfa	SH766062	Corris	O Very Small
Cwm Machno	SH750471	Betws y Coed	O Moderate M
Cwmmaengwynedd	SJ075326	Llangynog	U Small M
Cwmorthin	SH681459	Bl. Ffestiniog	O Large M
Cwm Teigl	SH736446	Ffestiniog	U Very Small M
Cwm y Foel	SH658476	Llanfrothen	O Very Small
Cwt y Bugail	SH734468	Bl. Ffestiniog	U Moderate M
Cyfannedd	SH631125	Fairbourne	U Very Small
Cymerau	SH777106	Corris	U Small M
Daren	SH721058	Corris	O & U Small M
Ddôl	SH560604	Llanberis	O Small M
Deeside	SJ138404	Corwen	O Small M
Dolbadau	SN198429	Cardigan	O Very Small
Dinorwig	SH595603	Llanberis	O Exc'y Large M
Diphwys	SH712463	Bl. Ffestiniog	U Very Large M
Dolfriog	SH611458	Beddgelert	O Very Small
Dolgarth	SH538495	Tremadoc	O Small
Dorothea	SH500532	Penygroes	O Very Large M
Drum	SH735431	Ffestiniog	U Small M
Era	SH760064	Corris	O Small M
Faenol	SH578615	Llanberis	O Small M
Foel	SH717556	Capel Curig	O Small M
Foelgron	SH744428	Ffestiniog	U Small M
Fedw	SH748525	Dolwyddelan	O Very Small
Ffridd	SH573526	Beddgelert	O Very Small
Ffridd Olchfa	SH603191	Barmouth	O Very Small
Fforest	SN190450	Cardigan	O Small M
Ffynnon Badarn	SH775114	Corris	U Very Small
Foel Gron	SH744428	Ffestiniog	O Small
Fotty	SH706465	Bl. Ffestiniog	O Moderate M
Fron	SH515548	Penygroes	O Small M
Fronboeth	SH652448	Llanfrothen	U Small M

Fron Goch	SH664972	Pennal	U Small M
Fronheulog	SN600998	Tywyn	U Very Small
Fronlog	SH489517	Penygroes	O Small M
Gaewern	SH745086	Corris	U Moderate M
Gallt y Fedw	SH499535	Penygroes	U Small M
Gallt y Llan	SH601583	Llanberis	O Very Small
Garreg Fawr	SH538582	Caernarfon	O Small M
Gartheiniog	SH822117	Dinas Mawddwy	O Small M
Gelli	SH637463	Llanfrothen	U Small
Gerynt	SH631484	Beddgelert	O Small M
Glandyfi	SN698961	Machynlleth	O Small M
Glanrafon	SH581540	Beddgelert	O Moderate M
Gloddfa Coed	SH493532	Penygroes	O Small M
Gloddfa Ganol	See Mathew's		
Gloddfa Glai	See Coed Madog		
Glogue	SN220327	Cardigan	O Small M
Glynrhonwy Upper	SH565607	Llanberis	O Small M
Glynrhonwy Lower	SH570610	Llanberis	O Moderate M
Gollellog	SH709019	Pennal	O Very Small
Golwern	SH621122	Fairbourne	O Small M
Goodman's	SH572606	Llanberis	O Small M
Gorseddau	SH573453	Tremadog	O Small M
Graig Ddu	SH724458	Bl. Ffestiniog	O Moderate M
Gwanas	SH798160	Dolgellau	O Small M
Gwernor	SH510526	Penygroes	O Small M
Hafodboeth	SH638418	Llanfrothen	U Very Small
Hafodlas	SH489540	Penygroes	O Moderate M
Hafod Las	SH779562	Betws-y-coed	O Small M
Hafod y Llan	SH613524	Beddgelert	O Small M
Hafod y Wern	SH530571	Caernarfon	O Small M
Hafod Uchaf	SH643434	Llanfrothen	U Very Small
Hafoty	SH632436	Penrhynd'draeth	O Small M
Henddol	SH619122	Fairbourne	O & U Small M
Hendre	SH698512	Dolwyddelan	O Very Small
Hendre Ddu	SH519444	Porthmadog	O Small M
Hendre Ddu	SH799125	Dinas Mawddwy	U Small M
Hollands	See Cesail		

Llangolman	SN130271	Fishguard	O Very Small M
Llaneilian	SH481932	Amlwch	O Very Small
Llanfair	SH580288	Harlech	U Small M
Llanfflewyn	SH347892	Amlwch	O Very Small
Llechan	SH756757	Conwy	O Very Small
Llechwedd	SH700470	Bl. Ffestiniog	U Very Large M
Llidiart yr Arian	SH633433	Llanfrothen	U Very Small
Llwyngwern	SH757045	Corris	O Small M
Llwydcoed	SH470508	Penygroes	O Small M
Llwynpiod	SN433299	Carmarthen	O Small M
Llyn Lagai	SH651485	Llanfrothen	O Very Small
Llyn y Gadair	SH564519	Beddgelert	O & S Small M
Maenofferen	SH714465	Bl. Ffestiniog	U Very Large M
Maes y Gamfa	SH818127	Dinas Mawddwy	O Small M
Manod	SH725452	Bl. Ffestiniog	O Small
Marchlyn	SH602628	Llanberis	O Small M
Mathew's	SH694470	Bl. Ffestiniog	U Very Large M
Minllyn	SH852139	Dinas Mawddwy	U Moderate M
Moel Faban	SH626678	Bethesda	U Small
Moelfre	SH521451	Tremadog	O Small M
Moelfferna	SJ125399	Corwen	U Moderate M
Moel Tryfan	SH515559	Penygroes	O Moderate M
Moelwyn	SH661442	Bl. Ffestiniog	U Small M
Moel y Faen	SJ185477	Llangollen	O Moderate M
Morben	SN716992	Machynlleth	O Small
Nantglyn	SH978598	Dinbych	O Very Small
Nantlle Vale	SH497524	Penygroes	O Small M
Nant y Fron	SH486518	Penygroes	O Moderate M
New Crown	SH513556	Penygroes	O Small M
Nantyr	SJ166384	Chirk	O Small
Nyth y Gigfran	SH689462	Bl. Ffestiniog	U Very Small
Oakeley — Rhiwbryfdir Cesail & Mathew's			U Extra large M
Oernant	SJ185469	Llangollen	O Small M
Old Pen y Bryn	SH502535	Penygroes	O Small M
Pantdreiniog	SH623671	Bethesda	O Small M
Pantmawr	SH658446	Llanfrothen	U Small M
Pantglas	SJ215478	Llangollen	O Small M
Parc	SH626436	Llanfrothen	U Small M
Parc (Old)	SH632444	Llanfrothen	O Small M

Penarth	SJ107424	Corwen	O&U Mod'ate M
Pencelli	SN199276	Cardigan	O Very Small
Penceulan	SN905536	Llanwrtyd	U Very Small
Penlan	SH760688	Trefriw	U Very Small
Penlan	SN207284	Cardigan	O Very Small
Penllyn	SH746522	Dolwyddelan	O Small
Penrhyn	SH620650	Bethesda	O Extra Large M
Penrhyngwyn	SH704149	Dolgellau	U Small M
Pen y Bryn	SH504538	Penygroes	O Moderate M
Pen y Ffridd	SH776612	Trefriw	O Small
Pen yr Orsedd	SH510538	Penygroes	O Large M
Plas y Nant	SH552562	Caernarfon	O Small
Porthgain	SM813325	Fishguard	O Small M
Portreuddyn	SH573409	Tremadog	O Very Small
Powys	SJ074294	Llangynog	O Very Small M
Prince of Wales	SH549498	Tremadog	O Moderate M
Prince Llywelyn	SH744528	Dolwyddelan	O & U Small M
Princess	SH553495	Tremadog	O Small
Ratgoed	SH787119	Corris	U Small M
Rhaeadr	SH682012	Pennal	O Very Small M
Rhiwbryfdir	SH693473	Bl. Ffestiniog	U Very Large M
Rhiwbach	SH740462	Bl. Ffestiniog	U Large M
Rhiwgoch	SH749537	Dolwyddelan	O Small M
Rhos	SH729564	Capel Curig	O Moderate M
Rhos Clogwyn	SH576530	Beddgelert	O Small
Rhosydd	SH664461	Bl. Ffestiniog	U Large M
Rosebush	SN079300	Fishguard	O Small M
Sealyham	SM960275	Haverfordwest	O Small M
South Dorothea	SH496531	Penygroes	O Moderate M
Tal y Fan	SH738733	Conwy	O Very Small
Tal y Sarn	SH495535	Penygroes	O Moderate M
Tan yr Allt	SH491523	Penygroes	O Small M
Tan y Bwlch	SH628683	Bethesda	U Moderate M
Treflan	SH539584	Caernarfon	O Small M
Trwynllwyd	SM832329	Fishguard	O Very Small
Twrch	SN145294	Cardigan	Very Small M
Tyddyn Shieffre	SH630135	Fairbourne	O Small M
Tŷ Mawr East	SH497524	Penygroes	O Very Small M
Tŷ Mawr West	SH496524	Penygroes	O Small M

Tŷ'n y Berth	SH738087	Corris	U Small M
Tyn y Bryn	SH742521	Dolwyddelan	O Small M
Tŷ'n y Ceunant	SH744088	Corris	O Very Small M
Tŷ'n y Coed	SH649148	Dolgellau	O Small
Tyn y Ffridd	SH628679	Bethesda	U Very Small M
Tyn y Garth	SN691945	Machynlleth	O Small
Tŷ'n y Weirglodd	SH494523	Penygroes	O Small M
Vivian	SH586604	Llanberis	O Moderate M
Voelgron	see Foelfron		
Votty	SH706465	Bl. Ffestiniog	U Moderate M
Welsh Slate	See Rhiwbr'dir		
Westminster	See Craig y Glem		
West Llangynog	SJ049259	Llangynog	U Small M .
Wrysgan	SH676458	Bl. Ffestiniog	U Moderate M
Wynne	SJ199379	Chirk	U Moderate M
Y Cefn	SH713421	Ffestiniog	O Very Small
Ystrad Ffin	SN787461	Llandovery	O Very Small

Some 'Off site' quarry mills

Escairgeiliog	SH759059	Mill for Cwm Gloddfa & Era
Nant y Pandy	SJ148417	Mill for Deeside
Pant yr Ynn	SH708454	Early mill for Diffwys
Pentrefelin	SJ218436	Mill used by Moel y Faen etc.
Pont Cyfyng	SH734570	Additional mill for Foel
Ynysypandy	SH550433	Mill for Gorseddau

Significant Independant Factory Sites

Clwt y Bont	SH572632	Writing Slate (?) factory
Crawia	SH536643/ 540641	Multi purpose factory
Groeslon	SH470551	Enamelling and general factory
Matthews Mill	SH768091	Enamelling and general factory
Rhyd y Sarn	SH690421	Very early saw mill

Other factories were sited at ports such as Deganwy, Port Dinorwig, Porthmadog, Port Penrhyn, and in towns such as Aberystwyth, Bangor, Blaenau Ffestiniog, Caernarfon, Machynlleth, Tywyn

Appendix 2

		t	c	q
Empresses	26 x 16	4	0	0
Princesses	24 x 14	3	5	0
Duchesses	24 x 12	2	15	0
Small Duchesses	22 x 12	2	10	0
Narrow Duchesses	22 x 11	2	5	0
(or Marchionesses)				
Broad Countesses	20 x 12	2	5	0
Countesses	20 x 10	1	15	0
Small Countesses	18 x 10	1	12	2
Viscountesses	18 x 9	1	7	2
Wide Ladies	16 x 10	1	7	2
Broad Ladies	16 x 9	1	5	0
Ladies	16 x 8	1	2	2
Small Ladies	14 x 8	1	0	1
Narrow Ladies	14 x 7	0	17	2
Doubles	12 x 6	0	14	0
Singles	10 x 5	0	9	3

These sizes varied from time to time and area to area. There was a semi-official Queen size which could be anything from 30 x 18 up to 36 x 26, Princesses were sometimes known as 'Fourteens', and the term 'Putts' was used for 14 x 12 and 'Ladies Putts' for 13 x 10, and 'Headers' for 14 x 12. Well before the end of the 19thC. these terms were dropped from official lists, but still remain in colloquial use.

There are now about 24 recognised sizes varying from 24 x 14 down to 10 x 6, in 'Best' and 'Strong' qualities. 'Damp Course' slates come in up to 10 sizes from 20 x 9 down to 9 x 4½.

* Weight declaration varied from time to time and from quarry to quarry, these were typical of the industry, Blaenau slates generally weighed about 7½% less than this. Lower qualities would be considerably heavier.

Slab, usually defined as slate ½" thick or more, ¼" was occasionally offered), and normally sold by weight (as were roofing slates in early times). Standard thicknesses were up to 2″ or 3″ in ½″ steps. Lots were generally of random sizes, sold by weight and priced according to the minimum size of pieces. Specified sizes attracted a surcharge. Semi-finished products were also sold by weight, fully finished items by count.

Special sizes could be very large, the biggest probably the 20′ x 10′ slab produced in 1862 at Clogau.

Slab weighs about 1 ton for 150 sq./ft per inch of thickness.

Poem said to have been written by Judge Leycester when staying with General Warburton whilst on Assize, early 19thC.

It has truly been said as we all must deplore,
That Grenville and Pitt have made peers by the score,
But now, 'tis asserted, unless I have blundered,
There's a man that makes peeresses here by the hundred,
He regards neither Portland, nor Grenville, nor Pitt,
But creates them at once without patent or writ;
By a stroke of a hammer without the King's aid,
A lady, a countess, or a duchess is made.
Yet high is the station from which they are sent,
And all their great titles are got by descent;
And where'er they are seen in palace or shop,
Their rank they preserve, and are still at the top.
Yet no merit they claim from their birth or connection,
But derive their chief worth from their native complexion,
And all the best judges prefer, it is said,
A countess in blue to a duchess in red.
This countess or lady though crowds may be present,
Submits to be dressed by the hands of a peasant.
And you'll see, when her grace is but once in his clutches,
With how little respect he will handle a duchess.
Close united they seem, and yet all who have tried 'em
Soon discover how easy it is to divide 'em.
The countess wants life, and the duchess is flat,
No spirit they have — they're as thin as a lath;

No passion or warmth to the countess is known,
And here grace is as cold and as hard as a stone;
Yet I fear you will find, if you watch them a little,
That the countess is frail, and the duchess is brittle.
Too high for a trade, yet without any joke,
Though they never are bankrupt, they often are broke,
And though not a soul ever pilfers or cozens,
They are daily shipped off and transported by dozens.
In France, Jocobinical France, we have seen,
How Nobles have bled by the fierce Guillotine,
But's what the French engine of death to compare,
To the engine which Greenfield and Bramah prepare?[1]
That democrat engine, by which we all know,
Ten thousand great duchesses fall at one blow.
And long may that engine its wonders display,
Long level with ease all rocks in its way,
Till the Vale of Nant Fracon its slates is bereft,
Nor Lady nor Countess nor Duchess is left.

[1] Greenfield, manager of Penrhyn quarry. Bramah, inventor of an (unsuccessful) screw-jack for prising out slate blocks.

Appendix 3

Outputs and Manning of North Wales Slate Quarries 1883

		tons	men	t/man
Bethesda				
Penrhyn	Lord Penrhyn	111,167	2838	39
Bryn Hafod y Wern		1,263	54	23
Pantdreiniog	J. Williams	245	13	19
Llanberis				
Dinorwig	G.W. Assheton-Smith	85,000	2710	31
Cefn Ddu	Llanberis Slate Co	4,040	172	23
Upper Glynrhonwy	Upper Glynrhonwy Slate Co	2,072	80	26
Glynrhonwy	Glynrhonwy Slate Co	1,789	70	25
Cook & Ddol		631	26	24
Caermenciau	Caermenciau Slate Q Co	300	12	25
Brynmawr	Bryn Mawr Slate Co.	160	?	-
Nantlle				
Dorothea	Dorothea Slate Quarry	15,841	481	33
Pen yr Orsedd	Penyrorsedd Slate Q Co	8,257	230	36
Pen y Bryn	Pen y Bryn Slate Co	5,083	240	21
Cilgwyn	Cilgwyn Slate Co	4,956	215	23
Alexandra	Alexandra Slate Co	3,721	182	20
Coed Madog	Coed Madog Slate Co	2,879	135	21
Braich	Braich Slate Co	2,200	99	22
Moel Tryfan	Moel Tryfan S S Q Co	1,781	70	25
South Dorothea	South Dorothea Slate Co	1,750	92	19
Fronlog	New Fronheulog Slate Co	1,364	69	20
Fron	Vron & Old Braich W S Q Co	650	?	
Caermenciau		300	12	25
Brynfferam	Brynfferam Slate Co	252	18	14
Nantlle Vale	Nantlle Vale Slate Quarry Co	150	20	7

Llwyd Coed	W. Jones	78	6	13

Conwy Valley

Prince Llywelyn	Prince Llewelyn Slate Co	1,315	42	31
Rhos	Capel Curig Slate Quarry Co	1,005	40	25
Hafod Las	Betws-y-coed Slate & S Co	289	11	26

Cwm Gwyrfai

Glanrafon	Glanrafon Slate Quarry Co	1,725	92	19
Plas y Nant	Plas y Nant Slate Co	672	28	24
Bwlch y Ddwy Elor		160	7	23
Garreg Fawr	Betws Garmon Slate Co	96	6	16

Cwm Pennant

Prince of Wales	?		9	

Blaenau Ffestiniog

Rhiwbryfdir	Welsh Slate Co	26,108	655	40**
Llechwedd	J.W. Greaves & Sons	24,723	553	45
Cesail	Oakeley Slate Quarries	13,372	507	26
Votty & Bowydd	Votty & Bowydd S Q	11,923	374	32
Gloddfa Ganol	Oakeley Slate Quarries	11,617	345	34
Cwmorthin	Cwmorthin Slate Co	10,709	441	24
Maenofferen	Maenofferen Slate Quarry	8,230	244	34
Diffwys	Diffwys Casson Slate Co	5,656	228	25
Rhosydd	New Rhosydd S Q Co	5,587	181	31
Rhiwbach	Ffestiniog Slate Co	3,187	130	24
Cwt y Bugail	Bugail Slate Co	1,662	40	41
Wrysgan	Wrysgan Slate Co	1,396	51	27
Craig Ddu	Craig Ddu Slate Co	807	36	22
Parc	J. Staveley	351	15	23
Conglog	New Conglog S & Slab Co	313	17	18
Voelgron	Jones & Owen	112	4	28
Bwlch y Slaters	Bwlch y Slaters Quarry Co	71	?	-

Corris

Braich Goch	Braich Goch Slate Quarry Co	5,085	238	21
Aberllefenni	R.D. Pryce	4,814	178	27
Abercwmeiddaw	Abercwmeiddaw S Q Co	2,875	80	36
Llwyngwern		915	35	26
Cymerau	H.N. Hughes	762	29	26
Ratgoed	H.N. Hughes	382	8	48 (?)

South Meirionnydd

Bryneglwys	W McConnel	7,996	282	28
Minllyn	Carlyle Slate & Slab Co	1,468	71	21
Hendre Ddu		878	36	24
Henddol	Walker & Co	401	40	10
Cwm Ebol	Cwmebol Slate Co	260	9	29
Gartheiniog	Jenkins & Owen	250	9	28
Penrhyngwyn		54	20	3
Golwern	Walker & Co	50	4	13

East Meirionnydd (Now Clwyd)

Moelfferna	M'lfferna & D'side S & S Co	1,601	81	20
Deeside	M'lfferna & D'side S & S Co	600	34	18
Penarth	Jones & Phillips	498	10	50
Cletwr	Llandderfel Slate & Slab Co	12	3	4

Dinbych & Monts

Moel y Faen		1,625	84	19
Clogau (Berwyn)		1,022	75	14
Hendre Ddu		878	?	-
Pant Glas		731	35	21
Craig Rhiwarth		329	15	22
Cwmmaengwynedd		10	2	5

** The quite good productivity at WSC even after the Big Fall was due to much of the fallen rock which had to be cleared, being useable block.

Gallt y Llan, Allt Goch, Foel, Talysarn, Hafodlas, Tŷ'n y Weirglodd, Cwmmachno & Hendre reported outputs for 1882 but not 1883.

Appendix 4

List of Manning and Outputs of Meirionnydd
Underground Slate Quarries 1895

	Men below ground	Men above ground	Tonnage	Tons per man
Blaenau Ffestiniog				
Oakeley (Rhiwbryfdir Cesail, Gloddfa Ganol)	736	916	56589	34
Llechwedd	222	264	15615	32
Votty & Bowydd	251	212	14537	31
Maenofferen	167	161	11047	34
Cwmorthin	183	108	6910	24
Rhosydd	108	78	4962	27
Wrysgan	41	55	3006	31
Diffwys	57	29	1136	13
Parc	14	15	409	14
Bwlch y Slaters	5	11	270	17
Moelwyn	4	-	76	
Manod	2	-	-	
Fronboeth		1	-	
Conglog	-	-	-	
Foelgron	-	-	-	
Corris				
Braich Goch	58	90	6044	41
Aberllefenni	73	59	4440	34
Abercorris	14	21	384	11
Cymerau	11	10	530	25
Ratgoed	7	5	232	19

South Meirionnydd

Bryneglwys	97	88	6385	34
Minllyn	12	8	550	27
Penrhyngwyn	3	-	4	
Henddol	-	1	-	

East Meirionnydd (now Clwyd)

Moelfferna	40	84	4955	40
Penarth	-	-	-	

Whilst some caution is needed when comparing tonnages per man, as these could vary considerably from year, it is clear that some, notably Llechwedd, were unable to maintain the productivities of earlier years. Abercorris is low as an abandoned working was being redeveloped. Braich Goch and Moelfferna were boosted by a high proportion of slab product. As with the 1883 figures, it is clear that generally large units were more efficient than small units.

Appendix 5

List of North Wales Slate Quarries, and Numbers Employed, 1937

Proprietor	Quarry	Men	District Total	Men %
Llanberis				
Sir Charles Assheton-Smith	Dinorwig	2369		
T. Owen	Upper Glynrhonwy	2	2371	29%
Bethesda				
Lord Penrhyn	Penrhyn	1916	1916	23%
Blaenau Ffestiniog				
Oakeley Slate Quarries	Oakeley, Diffwys	765		
J.W. Greaves & Sons	Llechwedd	438		
Maenofferen S Qs	Maenofferen	429		
Votty & Bowydd Qs	Votty & Bowydd	314		
Craig Ddu Slate Qs	Craig Ddu	95		
Manod Slate Quarries	Bwlch y Slaters	65		
Cwt y Bugail	Cwt y Bugail	41		
Wrysgan	Wrysgan	27	2174	26%
Nantlle				
Dorothea Slate Quarries	Dorothea, Gallt, Y Fedw, Pen y Bryn, South Dorothea	359		
Pen yr Orsedd S Q	Pen yr Orsedd	351		
Caernarvonshire Crown	Alexandra, Cilgwyn New Crown, Moel Tryfan	185		
Tyn y Weirglodd Q	Tŷ'n Weirglodd	39		

Vronlog Green	Fronlog	36		
W.R. Morris	Tan yr Allt	11		
Gloddfa Coed S Q	Gloddfa Coed	9		
O.J. Hughes	Fron	7		
Gallt y Llan Slate Quarry	Gallt y Llan	3	1000	12%

Dinbych

Glyn Quarries	Cambrian	121		
Moelfferna & Deeside S & S	Moelfferna	98		
B.B. Bevan	West Llangynog	22	241	4%

Corris

Braichgoch S & S Quarries	Braich Goch, Abercorris	101		
Aberllefenny S & S	Aberllefenni	131		
Ratgoed Quarries	Ratgoed	15	247	3%

Dyffryn Conwy

Cwm Machno S Q	Cwm Penmachno	123		
Rhos Slate Quarry	Rhos	52	175	2%

South Meirionnydd

Abergynolwyn S & S	Bryneglwys	58		
Bowley's Quarry	Gartheiniog	26		
T.O. Williams	Hendre Ddu	15	99	1%

Total 8223

As complied by D. Dylan Pritchard,
Quarry Manager's Journal 1943

Appendix 6

Glossary of Some Terms used in the Slate Industry

Agor	Opening. Chamber in underground quarry.
Agor i'r dydd	Open to the day. An underground working which breaks out to the surface.
Ar ei dannedd	In the teeth. Working against the cleavage.
Ar ei gorwedd	Lying. Sloping vein.
Ar ei phen	On its head. Vertical vein.
Bodiau	Damp inclusions on slate, if across the cleavage make block unsuitable.
Blocyn Tin	'Bottom Block'. A slate splitter's seat.
Bôn	Stump. Underlying rock. Or end face of a block.
Bonau	Discontinuities running across the cleavage, helpful for extracting blocks. (foot joints)
Bonc	Terrace.
Brigog	Applied to exposed rock damaged by weathering.
Bwrdd llif	Saw table.
Bwrdd plaen	Planing machine.
Canlyn wagan	Lazy worker (lit. Wagon follower)
Carped Lin	Knee Carpet. Sack used to protect the knee whilst splitting.
Cefnau	Joints in rock, across cleavage can be helpful for removal.
Ceiliog	Cockerel. Tall projecting rock.
Chwarel	General name for any quarry.
Cowjian	Thin chisel used for splitting blocks.
Crapfeydd	Big cracks which can cause rockfalls.
Creigwr	Rockman, actual extractor of rock.
Crybiau	Discontinuities which if far apart can help block extraction.

Crych croes	'Bending' of cleavage plane rendering the rock unusable.
Cyllel naddu	Chipping knife. The tool for the hand-trimming of roofing slate.
Cŷn Brasholt	Fat wedge. Wide wedge for splitting blocks.
Cŷn Manholt	Small wedge. Wide and slim chisel used for splitting roofing slates.
Chwarelwr	Splitter or any quarry worker.
Chwimsi	(horse) whim.
Defnyn	Depth, applied to floors or levels underground.
Drifrigo	Removal of overburden.
Dynion yr Injan	Steam engine attendant or any Mill worker.
Gafael da	A good hold, applied to an effective blast.
Gloddfa	A 'digging', usually applied to underground quarries.
Gollwng	Crewling wagons down an incline (lit. drop).
Gordd y twll	Quarry hammer. Sledge-type hammer used for breaking rock.
Gordd y wal	Hammer used for splitting.
Graig	Rock. Can also mean quarry.
Gwaith	Works. Can mean the mill or the entire quarry.
Gwal	An open-fronted shed where slates were split and trimmed, literally a 'Wall', but may be a corruption of Gwâl, a 'Lair'.
Gwythiennau	Thin bands of intrusive material running through slate.
Hogia'r Twll	Pit workers (derogatory term for Nantlle men).
Hollti	The splitting (of slate).
Hwrdd	Sandsaw (lit. Ram).
Inclên	Incline.

Lamp	Overseer in an underground working, deriving from the carbide lamp carried during his daily visits to each chamber.
Lefal	Level. Usually a tunnel in an underground working.
Lle brwnt	Cruel place. Awkwardly situated rock.
Llond het	Hatful. Derisorily small quantity, usually applied to a disappointing blast.
Llygad	Eye, or best part. The actual Vein.
Maen Nâdd	Stone used as seat by splitters.
Melin	Mill.
Mochyn	Pig. The iron weighted balancing trolley of a Mass Balanced Incline.
Morthwl dragio	Tearing hammer. A short hammer used for driving wedges to break rock.
Miniar	Sharpened. A very stubbly chisel used for splitting rock.
Mwynwr	Miner, specialist employed to cut tunnels through country rock, paid by yardage.
Palffiau	Faults in cleavage, only apparent when splitting.
Pendrwm	Top-heavy. Overhanging rock.
Pincin	Pinnacle. Vertical piece of rock.
Piser	Can for carrying tea.
Plwg ac adain	Plug and feathers. A tool consisting of an inner tapered pin surrounded by a tapered sleeve, split longitudinally, which when hammered into a crevice or drilled hole, will expand initiating a crack.
Plyg	Fold. A quantity of rock obtained from the face.
Pric mesur	Measure stick. The serrated stick, with a nail at one end used for marking out a roofing slate for trimming.
Rhys	A massive, iron bound, African oak mallet which skilfully used could break a block.

Rwb	A (usually small) rockfall.
Rwbblwr	Rubbler. The unskilled man or young learner who removed waste rock.
Sawdl	Heel. Lowest part of a face to be worked.
Sefyll ar y troed	Standing on its foot. Vertical vein.
Sinc	Sink. A pit working.
Slontiau	Breaks of direction in cleavage causing a bad split.
Taflu dros y droed	Throwing over the foot. Overhanging rock.
Talcan	Forehead. Towering mass or rock. Also used to describe the end of a block.
Tâl mawr	Big pay. The Bargainer's 4 weekly settlement which (hopefully) was larger than the 3 interim payments. Traditionally the weekend when outer clothing was washed and ironed.
Tir sâl	Bad ground.
Tomen	Waste heap, rubbish run.
Trafael	The bench with fixed iron blade, used in conjunction with the *cyllell* for hand-trimming roofing slate.
Trwnc	The table of a table incline.
Tryc dŵr	Water balance tank (lit. water truck).
Tun bwyd	Food tin, usually oval-ended.
Twll	Hole. A pit working.
Tŷ gof	Smithy.
Tŷ Injan	Engine house, or any building containing machinery.
Tyllu	Drilling (of shot holes).
Walet	Wallet. A cloth double sack, carried on the shoulder. Used by barracking men to carry their food supplies for the week.
Ysmotiau	Roundish green or grey spots on the slate.

Appendix 7

An account of a visit to the Welsh Slate Company's
quarry circa 1880

'While at Blaenau Ffestiniog we made our way to the Palmerston
Slate Quarry, which we were told was the largest and most
productive in Wales. The landlady of the Baltic Hotel found us a
highly respectable guide, who conducted us up the great heaps of
shale, and past the finishing sheds to a narrow-gauge line, along
which the huge blocks of slate are brought from the pit's mouth on
trucks. On one of these we were bidden to take our seats, the guide
sitting just behind us and holding us on carefully, whilst two lads
pushed us along through a tunnel about 50 yards long, dark and
rather moist. On reaching our destination, where we came to more
sheds filled with machinery, we alighted and walked down some
steps into the first chamber of the black smoky mine; there are nine
beneath it, right into the bowels of the earth. The miners, who
number between seven and eight hundred, were then enjoying the
open air during their dinner hour, and were sitting or lying about
near the pit's mouth. Considering the fearful atmosphere so many
of them have to work in from six in the morning till 5.30 in the
evening, they, most of them, looked very robust and healthy; they
were all very civil and well behaved to us as we passed in and out
amongst them, and there seemed a good deal of kindly feeling and
good fellowship between themselves. The miners earn from 23s. to
25s. a week, and the slate finishers 45s. This mine made £83,000
clear profits last year, but this was unusually good. It yields an
average profit of £50,000 or £60,000. The shaft we went down was
pitch dark, and the air was most disagreeable to breath. A miner
lad went before us with a lantern; our guide held me by the arm and
my sister followed us closely, carrying a bit of lighted candle, set in
a lump of clay, in her hand. We came upon bridges across shafts
letting air down to the chambers beneath, where we saw, dimly
burning, ever so far down, the lights of the poor miners. The

quality of the slate in this quarry is very good, and the mine has already been worked 80 years. Our guide showed us the water-works which pump the water out of the mine, and the slate just as it is after it has been blasted, huge blocks worth about £4 each, which are conveyed to the pit's mouth on trucks, part of the way drawn by horses and then by machinery with wire ropes up the steep incline to where the narrow-gauge line takes it to the finishing sheds where it is split, cut in squares, and then taken off to the railroad, to be forwarded to all parts of the world. We took a look at the great engine which sets all the different machinery in motion in the finishing shed, where nothing is done by hand now-a-days except the actual splitting of the blocks of slate, which is an easy task when once the two wedges are driven in. The guide has a fixed charge of 5s. for taking people over the mine, and we were glad to give it to him — he was so civil and so careful over us.'

From Thorough Guides, North Wales, Part 1 1892 pp178/9

SOURCES
SELECTED BIBLIOGRAPHY

Anon, *Cambrian Tourist*, (Whittaker, 1828)

Anon, *Black's Guide Through Wales*, Black, 1860)

Anon, *Handbook for Travellers, N. Wales*, (Murray, 1885)

Anon, *Industrial and Independent Locomotives and Railways of North Wales*, (Birmingham Loco. Club, 1968)

Anon, *A Return to Corris*, (Corris Rly Soc 1988)

Baddley & Ward, *Through Guide, North Wales, Vol 1.*, (Dulau & Co. 1892)

Bennett, G.J., *Pedestrian's Guide Through N. Wales*, (Colburn, 1838)

Bingley, W., *A Tour Round Wales (1st ed.)*, (Bingley, 1800)

Boyd, J.I.C., *The Ffestiniog Railway*, (Oakwood Press, 1975)

Carrington, D.C., *Delving in Dinorwig*, (Gwasg Carreg Gwalch, 1994)

Davies, D.C., *Slate & Slate Quarrying*, (Crosby, Lockwood 1878)

Davies, D.L., *The Glyn Valley Tramroad*, (Oakwood Press, 1966)

Davies, J., *A History of Wales*, (Allen Lane, 1993)

Dodd, A.H., *The Ind. Revolution in N. Wales*, (U of W Press, 1971)

Dodd, A.H., *History of Caernarvonshire 1284-1900*, (Caerns Hist. Soc. 1968)

Eames, A. & Hughes, *Porthmadog Ships*, (Gwynedd A.S., 1975)

Eames, A., *Heb Long Wrth y Cei*, (Gwasg Carreg Gwalch, 1991)

Holmes, A., *Slates from Abergynolwyn*, (Gwynedd A S, 1986)

Hughes, G., *House on a Hill*, (S.N.P. Study Centre, 1989)

Hughes, J.E. & B., *Chwarel y Penrhyn*, (Penrhyn Quarry Ltd, 1979)

Isherwood, G., *Cwmorthin Slate Quarry*, (Meirioneth Field Study, 1982)

Isherwood, G., *Slate*, (A.B. Publishing, 1988)

Jenkinson, H.I., *North Wales*, (Stanford, 1878)

Jones, E., *Bargen Dinorwig*, (Tŷ a'r Graig, 1980)

Jones, G.R., *Chwarel Blaenycwm*, (Ff P T B, 1992)

Jones, I.W., *Eagles Do Not Catch Flies*, (J.W. Greaves & Sons, 1986)

Jones, I.W., *The Llechwedd Strike 1893*, (Llechwedd Publications, 1993)

Jones, R.M., *The North Wales Quarrymen 1874-1922*, (U of W Press, 1982)

Lewis, M.J.T. (Ed), *The Slate Quarries of N. Wales 1873*, (S N P Study Centre, 1987)

Lewis & Denton, *Rhosydd Slate Quarry*, (The Cottage Press, 1974)

Lindsay, J., *History of the N. Wales Slate Ind.*, (David & Charles, 1974)

Lindsay, J., *The Great Strike 1900-1903*, (David & Charles, 1987)

Lloyd, L., *The Unity of Barmouth*, (Gwynedd A S, 1977)

Lloyd, L., *The Port of Caernarfon 1793-1900*, (Lloyd, 1989)

Lloyd, L., *Pwllheli The Port and Mart·of Llŷn*, (Lloyd, 1991)

Lloyd, L., *Wherever Freights May Offer*, (Lloyd, 1993)

North, F.J., *Slates of Wales*, (Nat. Mus. of Wales, 1925)

Owen, R., *Diwydiannau Col*

Parry, B.R. (Ed), *Chwareli a Chwarelwyr*, (Gwynedd A S, 1977)

Pennant, T., *A Tour of Wales MDCCLXIII (1st ed)*, (T. Hughes, 1778)

Rees, D.M., *The Industrial Archaeology of Wales*, (David & Charles, 1975)

Pritchard, D.D., *The Slate Industry of North Wales*, (Gwasg Gee, 1946)

Richards, A.J., *Gazeteer of the Welsh Slate Industry*, (Gwasg Carreg Gwalch, 1991)

Richards, A.J., *Slate Quarrying at Corris*, (Gwasg Carreg Gwalch, 1994)

Roberts, R.O., *Farming in Caernarvonshire around 1800*, (Caerns R O, 1973)

Senior, M., *Harlech & Lleyn*, (Gwasg Carreg Gwalch, 1988)

Stack, B., *Handbook of Mining Machinery*, (J. Wiley & Sons)

Story, A.T., *North Wales*, (Methuen, 1907)

Tomos, D., *Llechi Lleu*, (Argraffdy Arfon, 1980)

Williams, G.J., *Hanes Plwyf Ffestiniog*, (Hughes & Son, 1880)

Williams, M., *The Slate Industry*, (Shire Publications, 1991)

Williams, E. Elis, *Bangor, Port of Beaumaris*, (Gwynedd A S, 1988)

Williams & Lewis, *Pioneers of Ffestiniog Slate*, (Plas Tan y Bwlch, 1987)

Williams & Lewis, *Gwydir Slate Quarries*, (Plas Tan y Bwlch, 1989)

OTHER SOURCES

Public Reports

Report of the Departmental Commitee upon Merionethshire Slate Mines 1895

Inspector of Mines Reports 1875 on.

Private Reports

Chwarel y Diphwys	Plas Tan y Bwlch, 1983
Chwareli a Mwyngloddiau Eryri a'i Gyffiniau (M. Williams)	Plas Tan y Bwlch, 1985
Cwt y Bugail/Blaen y Cwm	Plas Tan y Bwlch, 1985
Chwarel Foel/Chwarel Rhos	Plas Tan y Bwlch, 1986
Chwarel Blaenycwm (G.R. Jones)	Ff PTB, 1991
Rhiwbach	Ff PTB, 1992

Papers and Articles

Crossland, T.P., *Internal Combustion Locos in Slate Mines*, (Q M J, August, 1932)

Edwards, I., *Slate Quarries in the Llangollen Dist. Denbighshire Hist. Soc.*

Foster, F.W., *A Simple Water Balance*, (Q M J, May, 1938)

Griffith, I., *Recent Developments in the Slate Industry of North Wales*, (Q M J, June, 1933)

Herbert, S., *Modernisation of a Welsh Slate Quarry*, (Q M J, Nov., 1972)

Houston, W.J., *New Developments at Dorothea SQ*, (Q M J, Feb., 1964)

Jones, G.P., *The Gwernor Slate Quarry*, (Transactions CHS, 1987)

Kellow, J., *The Slate Trade of N. Wales*, (Mining Journal, 1868)

Kellow, M., *The Application of Mechanical Means to Quarrying Slate*, (Q M J, June, 1933)

O'Neill, H., *The Llechwedd Slate Mine*, (Q M J, Nov., 1959)

O'Neill, H., *The Dinorwig Slate Quarry*, (Q M J, Dec., 1959)

Owen, E., *The Penrhyn Quarry*, (The Red Dragon Vol. VII)

Pritchard, D.D., *The Early Days of the Slate Industry*, (Q M J, July, 1942)

Pritchard, D.D., *New Light on the History of the Penrhyn Slate Quarries in the 18thC.*, (Q M J, September, 1942)

Pritchard, D.D., *The Financial Structure of the Slate Industry et al*, (Q M J, Dec. 1942 — April 1943)

Pritchard, D.D., *Aspects of the Slate Industry*, (Q M J, 1943-45)

Pritchard, D.D., *A Plan for the Slate Industry*, (Q M J, May, 1946)

Williams-Ellis, M.I., *Mechanical Handling in Slate*, (Q M J, January, 1932)

Williams-Ellis, M.I., *The Llechwedd Slate Quarries*, (Q M J, June, 1933)

Journals

The Mining Journal, 1846-1891. Quarry Manager's Journal, Vols 14 on.
The Slate Trades Gazette 1912-1926.
Transactions of the Caernarfonshire Historical Society, Various
Transactions of the Merioneth Historical Society, Various

Theses

Pritchard, D., *The Slate Industry of North Wales 1780-1935*, (UCNW, 1935)
Ellis, G., *A History of the Slate Quarryman in Caernarfonshire in the 19th C.*, (UCNW, 1931)
Jones Evan, *The History of our Rocks and their Development*, (Inst. of Quarrying, 1926)

Archive Material

J.S. Wilkinson & other deposits Caernarfon R.O.
Various deposits   Dolgellau R.O.
Home Office lists of Mines, various dates.

U of W = University of Wales
A S = Archive Service
S N P = Snowdonia National Park
Ff P T B = Fforwm Plas Tan y Bwlch
Q M J = Quarry Managers' Journal

A Gazeteer of the Welsh Slate Industry

Alun John Richards

240 pages: many maps: £6.90 ISBN: 0-86381-196-5

This volume contains archaeological detail and brief historical notes of some 400-plus slate quarries and mills in Wales — every single site having been explored by Alun, usually accompanied by his patient wife. Divided into geographical sections, it represents some 20 years of fieldwork.

While not claiming to be exhaustive, the book is nevertheless the first work to bring the vast majority of the various locations together into one handy and affordable volume. It will supplement the various single-site or single-district works already published and hopefully provide a spur to researchers to produce others.

Slate Quarrying at Corris
Alun John Richards
Price: £5.45; many maps and illustrations; 144 pages; ISBN: 0-86381-279-1.

Slate Quarrying at Corris has a long, interesting and innovative, but hithertoe largely unrecorded history. Beginning in Tudor times, its saga continues to the present day. Output was never great and its days of prosperity were few, but to those who toiled to win its rock, many suffering death, disease or disablement, the quarries of Corris loomed as large in their lives as any of those in other, more widely publicised, areas.

**Other books of Welsh interest
send for our full catalogue:
GWASG CARREG GWALCH,
Iard yr Orsaf,
Llanrwst,
Gwynedd.
☎ 01492 642031
Ffacs: 01492 641502**